MW00657703

Badass Self-Care

Deanna,
You can trust yourself.
xo,
Melinda

Badass Self-Care:

A six-month guided journey into reclaiming self-love and self-trust

Melinda Scime

For more information, address:
melinda@melindascime.com

First edition November 2021

Book cover and interior design by Jacquelyn Tierney
Author photo on back cover by Andrea Costrino

ISBN 978-0-578-99973-9

www.melindascime.com

For girls and women everywhere,
May you know and trust your inner wisdom,
May you embody the truth that you are worthy of love and care,
May you reclaim your body, your voice, and your dreams.

Contents

Preface

I first coined the term Badass Self-Care as a promise to myself.

I was 35 years-old and had lost myself inside of caregiving for my children and my husband's 98 year-old grandmother who was staying with us. One of my daughters was a toddler and the other was a teenager and it makes my head spin every time I remember juggling all those stages of life at once.

After my husband's grandmother left (she had stayed with us for a little less than a year while her house was repaired after Hurricane Sandy), I promised myself that I would make myself more of a priority and tend to my own needs. I named my intention Badass Self-Care because taking care of myself felt like a radical notion and I knew I would need to channel my inner badass in order to start showing up for myself. I started making a list each week of self-care steps. I wrote in my journal, went to yoga class, met my girlfriends for brunch, meditated, and made myself beautiful green smoothies. I started to feel better - more centered and grounded, more connected to myself and what I wanted and needed.

I noticed that most women struggle with caring for themselves so I decided to teach what I had learned from my own experiences. The first version of Badass Self-Care was a six-week online course. We talked about resting and staying hydrated, mindful self-talk and releasing our old stories, creating boundaries and connecting with our intuition. It was a beautiful gathering of women. I was proud of what I had created and really thought I had self-care figured out.

I lived in that space for many years.

Then I landed in burn out.

I want to be able to explain exactly how and when it happened, but I can't. It wasn't because of any one particular event. It was a culmination of years of over-functioning and continuing to give when I had nothing left. I don't know how women are able to do this, but I know we are; we do it all the time. I was exhausted and physically unwell. I had an episode of depression for the first time in a decade. I was embarrassed and ashamed - how could this be happening to me when I teach other women how to care for themselves? I felt like a fraud.

I took a sabbatical from work. It was supposed to be so I could write my first book, *My Sacred Pause*, but I ended up devoting most of the three months off to my healing. I had lost myself again. It turns out the issue wasn't the stress of caring for a toddler, a teenager, and an elder; it was my pattern of ignoring my own needs. What shifted when I started talking about Badass Self-Care is that I did tend to my own needs (which was new) but only after taking care of everyone else first (a very old habit).

I blamed myself for my struggles. I believed that if I took the time for self-care practices then I should feel good, physically and emotionally. But there I was in burn out. I thought that there must be something wrong with *me*, that I had some inner flaw that made me "needy." I felt that *I* needed to change, to be less sensitive or somehow better adapt to life around me. The truth is there was another layer to my struggles with caring for myself that I had yet to unpack – the bullshit messaging of patriarchy. Specifically, I had internalized the belief that everyone else's needs were more important than my own and that my purpose and worth was tied to caring for others. Girls and women are socialized into this idea from a young age, especially when it comes to motherhood. We are taught that a "good woman/ mother" cares for others first and sacrifices her own needs. It's bullshit. And it's definitely *not* what I want to model for my daughters.

After many more years of therapy (and still going!), self-study (give me all the meditation and journal writing) and being brave (sometimes you just have to try things), I am changed.

My caregiving, my nurturing, my deep love and kindness now includes myself.

My definition of self-care has expanded beyond behaviors and into the profound work of self-love and self-trust.

My understanding of self-care now recognizes the impact of the sociocultural context we live in.

I now know that there are many things we can do to care for ourselves *and* that the systems we live inside of have a very real impact on our well-being.

Badass Self-Care has changed with me. What began as a six-week online course has developed into a six-month deep dive group offering. I have held space for the circle known as Badass Self-Care for five years now and each year the work evolves because as I learn and grow, I incorporate my deeper understanding of self-care into the work. In this moment, I feel the Badass Self-Care framework has reached a form of completion that has compelled me to write it down, to memorialize it here in this book. I also know that my understanding of self-care will likely evolve further as I learn more and continue on my own healing path. Ultimately, I would probably never write this book if I waited until I felt like I had reached my highest and most complete understanding of Badass Self-Care. This work is a lifelong journey and this book is a reflection of a moment in time. I offer it to you with deep love and in the spirit of walking this path together.

Melinda Scime
Niagara Falls, New York
September 2021

Welcome

I'm so glad that you are here! You have already begun your Badass Self-Care journey just by choosing to open this book. Getting started is often the hardest part so I invite you to pause, take a deep breath, and send yourself some love and appreciation.

The fact that you are reading these words lets me know that you are curious about self-care in one way or another. Perhaps the book title caught your eye or maybe you have been on the path of self-care for years. Wherever you are on your journey, you are welcome here and this book will be a helpful and supportive tool for you. My hope is that you will return to these pages often. In my experience with living by these concepts and teaching them to others, I have found that the same practices and prompts land differently and guide us to different places when revisited. This is why some women take my Badass Self-Care course multiple times: the material may be the same, but we are changed and that shifts our experience with the work.

What exactly is the work of Badass Self-Care?

Badass Self-Care is the practice of unpacking the bullshit messaging of patriarchy so that we can reclaim self-love and self-trust. It is sacred, slow work that goes beneath the surface of what you might think of as self-care. The practices and prompts in this book are an invitation to dive in deep and deconstruct the sociocultural messages that deliberately undermine your ability to care for yourself so that you can shift your mindset and ultimately, your life.

There are six components of Badass Self-Care: **Listen**, **Ground**, **Release**, **Speak**, **Act**, and **Honor**. **Listen** is the practice of turning inward and connecting with ourselves. **Ground** is the practice of cultivating a loving relationship with our bodies. **Release** is the practice of letting go of what no longer serves us. **Speak** is the practice of naming our desires and allowing ourselves to want. **Act** is the practice of taking steps toward our dreams and creating supportive structure in our lives. **Honor** is the practice of claiming our truth, celebrating ourselves, and honoring our feminine nature.

Note that each of those definitions includes the word "practice" because the work of Badass Self-Care *is* a practice. This path does not lead to a destination. There is no arriving and yet, you are already there. The work of reclaiming self-love and self-trust is not something you can complete and check off your to-do list; it is an ongoing, ever-evolving process of being in relationship with yourself.

Tenets of Badass Self-Care

1. You are enough, just as you are in this moment. Everything that you need is already within you.

2. You do not need to be fixed because you are not broken.

3. You deserve to be the center of your own life.

4. Self-care is not selfish.

5. Self-care is not an indulgence; it is a necessity.

6. Self-care occurs within the social and cultural context of our lives.

7. Self-care is not prescriptive; it is an individualized practice.

8. Self-care is dynamic and fluid; what it looks like changes over time, sometimes even moment to moment.

9. Self-care is not something we have to earn. We are all worthy of self-care simply because we exist.

10. Self-care is more than behaviors; it is a mindset, an embodied knowing of our worth.

How To Use This Book

I created this book to be a self-guided journey through the practices of Badass Self-Care. This book is designed as a six-month journey. My intention is that you will spend one month working with each of the Badass Self-Care components. The chapters are broken down into four weeks and each week has its own set of practices and journal prompts. I have included multiple pages of the Mindful Morning and Mindful Evening journal prompts (they vary a bit depending on the component you are working with) and the Release, Respond, Receive prompts (these are the same throughout the book). The book is not designed for you to write every day. You can write in response to a few different journal prompts throughout the week or do one or two longer writing sessions. You can also use your own journal if you prefer or need more room than I've allocated here. There is no right or wrong way to engage with the material. Experiment and find what works for you. Trust your own process.

There is a chart at the end of each month to help you track your Badass Self-Care practices. I included a monthly chart because charts motivate me! If charts are not for you, just skip it. There is nothing in this book that you *have* to do. The book is here to support you. Take what you need and leave the rest. If you do use the monthly charts, don't let them become something that you use to beat yourself up. Badass Self-Care is not about perfectionism and the expectation is *not* that you do the practices every day.

Badass Self-Care Assessment

This is not a traditional assessment. There aren't any right or wrong answers and you don't get a score at the end. Instead, the Badass Self-Care assessment is an invitation to notice what is true for you in this moment. Observe your responses with compassion and allow whatever arises for you to be information as you begin your Badass Self-Care journey.

Listen

Turning inward and connecting with ourselves.

	Never	*Rarely*	*Some-times*	*Often*	*Almost Always*
I spend time turned inward, connecting with myself.				☆	
My intuition guides my choices.			☆		
I meditate.		☆			
I have difficulty hearing my inner voice.			☆		
I trust myself.			☆		
I follow my gut.			☆		

Ground

Cultivating a loving relationship with our bodies.

	Never	*Rarely*	*Some-times*	*Often*	*Almost Always*
I know when I am thirsty.			☆		
I eat when I am hungry.				☆	
I get 7-9 hours of sleep per night.				☆	
I know what kind of movement feels good in my body.			☆		
I am dissatisfied with the size or shape of my body.					☆
I engage in a regular movement/ physical activity practice.		☆			
I appreciate my body.		☆			
I understand how the media influences my feelings about my body.				☆	

Release

Letting go of what no longer serves us.

	Never	*Rarely*	*Some-times*	*Often*	*Almost Always*
I hold on to things.			☆		
Thoughts replay in my mind over and over.				☆	
My living space feels peaceful and orderly.			☆		
It is hard for me to forgive myself.			☆		
My life is aligned with my priorities.			☆		
I have habits I'd like to change.					☆
I have tools or practices for releasing my emotions and cleansing my energy.			☆		

Speak

Naming our desires and allowing ourselves to want.

	Never	*Rarely*	*Some-times*	*Often*	*Almost Always*
I believe I am allowed to want.				☆	
I have clarity around my dreams and goals.		☆			
I know what I want.		☆			
I have trouble speaking up for myself.			☆		
My needs matter.				☆	
My dreams and goals are important.			☆		

Act

Taking steps toward our dreams and creating supportive structure in our lives.

	Never	*Rarely*	*Some-times*	*Often*	*Almost Always*
I set boundaries to protect my time and energy.		☆			
I create action plans to help me work toward my goals.		☆			
It's hard for me to say no.				☆	
I worry about letting others down.			☆		
I take time for myself.				☆	
I pursue my dreams.		☆			

Honor

Claiming our truth, celebrating ourselves, and honoring our feminine nature.

	Never	*Rarely*	*Some-times*	*Often*	*Almost Always*
I prioritize myself.			☆		
I have to work to earn worthiness.			☆		
I worry about not being good enough.			☆		
I love myself.				☆	
I celebrate my strengths.			☆		
When someone gives me a compliment, I brush it off or qualify it.			☆		
I embrace my feminine characteristics.				☆	

A Few Notes

First, my use of the words woman and women throughout the book refer to *all* women: cis and trans women, as well as those of any gender identity who experience misogyny like women do. Second, although I am a licensed psychologist, this book is not a substitute for therapy and does not constitute medical advice. Please seek help from a mental health professional if you are struggling with your mental health. Lastly, oftentimes personal and spiritual development focuses on the individual to the point of ignoring systems. Badass Self-Care is a framework that specifically aims to consider the impact of the systems we live inside of, particularly patriarchy. I have done my best to consider systems during the creation of this program and the writing of this book and yet, I know that there will places where I have fallen short because of my privilege as a cis-gendered, straight, white woman.

CHAPTER ONE

Listen

The first component of Badass Self-Care is **Listen**. **Listen** is the practice of turning inward and connecting with ourselves. It can be challenging to observe our own thoughts and feelings inside of modern daily life. Our minds are filled with to-do lists and our nervous systems are overwhelmed by the constant stimulation of technology. **Listen** is the practice of consciously carving out space to be with yourself. By nurturing your relationship with yourself, you will learn to hear your wise inner voice.

During this first month of Badass Self-Care, I am inviting you to connect with your intuition and come home to the wisdom that has always been inside of you. We all have an intuitive part, the part of us that just *knows* things without any logical or rational explanation. However, our culture does not set us up to connect with or live from this wise inner knowing. We struggle to trust ourselves because of society's messaging. Specifically, patriarchy teaches us to deny and devalue our feminine nature, including our intuition. We are taught to look for guidance and direction outside of ourselves, to turn toward outer authority figures such as parents, bosses, doctors, and teachers. Many of us ignore or turn away from our intuitive knowing in order to meet social expectations. **Listen** is about reclaiming our inner authority and cultivating self-trust.

We are all intuitive and have the ability to access the wise inner knowing that exists inside all of us. There are a variety of ways that you might experience your intuition. For some, intuition is experienced in the body. For example, it may arise as a feeling in your gut or a tingling in your hands. Others experience intuition as an inner voice, communicating with them through words. There is no right or wrong way to experience intuition. Simply set the intention to notice how your intuition communicates with you and be open to whatever arises.

Turning inward and connecting with yourself is a practice. Like all the components of Badass Self-Care, it is not something you achieve and then are done with. This practice of listening to your inner wise self is an ongoing learning. You may notice that your ability to connect with and be guided by your intuition varies by context. Perhaps you feel better able to access your intuition when it comes to parenting but struggle with being guided by your inner knowing in your professional life. Maybe you feel connected with your inner self when you are being creative and painting or writing but you find it difficult to maintain that connection when you are dealing with matters concerning your family of origin. I invite you to be patient with the process and practice self-compassion as you learn and grow.

I have come to the place where I live my life guided by my intuition. I practice turning inward and connecting with myself several times throughout the day. My decisions are guided by my wise inner knowing, whether I am choosing what to eat for lunch or making decisions about my business. But it was not always this way.

I spent almost the first 30 years of my life disconnected from my intuition. I was focused on pleasing others, achieving as much as possible in an attempt to prove my worth, and meeting the expectations of society. On paper, I had succeeded. I had recently finished my doctorate in psychology and started a job in my field. I had been offered a promotion that came with a substantial increase in salary and responsibility. Yet, I was often physically ill, exhausted, and anxious. I spent many days crying in my fancy office. I was confused. I felt like I had done everything "right" and couldn't understand why I felt so much discontent.

A few months before my 30th birthday, I gifted myself with a yoga retreat. During the retreat we did a meditation about our ideal day and what we truly desired. It was the first time I allowed myself to think about what I really wanted, not what I thought I was supposed to do or what others expected of me. When I turned inward, the answers were right there waiting for me. I knew what I wanted. I wanted to spend more time with my family. I wanted to teach yoga. I wanted more ease and joy in my life. It was like a layer of film was removed and I could see clearly for the first time.

I came home from the retreat and knew that I could not follow through with the promotion. I had heard the voice of my soul and I vowed I would not abandon her again. A few months later I told my boss I did not want the promotion. Instead, I cut back to part-time at my job and opened a yoga studio. The following year I left my job, started a private practice as a therapist, and opened my dream wellness center. Don't worry - I am not asking you to turn your life upside down! The practice of listening to your inner self does not always have this type of dramatic impact. You may not have a big epiphany and decide to change your life. Instead, it might create a small shift. Whatever your experience is, turning inward and connecting with your inner wise self is a powerful practice. You are learning to trust yourself.

There are many ways to connect with your inner self and cultivate a relationship with your intuition. I suggest trying all of this month's practices and then choosing one or two to incorporate into your daily routine.

Week 1

PRACTICE:

Do nothing. Carve out 5-15 minutes and practice doing nothing. Simply sit and be with yourself. It might help to set a timer so that you're not constantly checking the clock. If this feels challenging, know that you are not alone. You can couple this practice with something you already do, such as walking or taking a bath. The idea is simply to set everything aside and just be with yourself for a few minutes. Notice whatever arises for you during this practice without any judgment or expectations.

JOURNAL PROMPTS:

What is your current relationship with your intuition?

MINDFUL MORNING

Journal Practice: Listen

date: ______

My intention for today: ______

Some actions to support my intention: ______

An affirmation to support my intention: ______

One self-care step I will take today: ______

One thing I am looking forward to today: ______

One thing I am grateful for today: ______

MINDFUL EVENING

date: ____________

Journal Practice: Listen

The best part of today: ______________________________

____

____

____

The hardest part of today: ______________________________

____

____

____

I'm proud of myself for: ______________________________

____

____

____

Pause and take three deep breaths. Tune into yourself. What are the words you need to hear right now? Write them here: ______________________________

____

____

____

____

____

Three things I am grateful for in this moment: ______________________________

____

____

____

____

RELEASE, RESPOND, RECEIVE

Journal Practice

date: ____________

Release: let everything out, write down whatever is on your mind

Respond: pause and connect with your wise self, respond to the things you've written above

Receive: list at least three things you are grateful for in the moment

RELEASE, RESPOND, RECEIVE

Journal Practice

date: ____________

Release: let everything out, write down whatever is on your mind

Respond: pause and connect with your wise self, respond to the things you've written above

Receive: list at least three things you are grateful for in the moment

MINDFUL MORNING

Journal Practice: Listen

date: ____________

My intention for today: ____________

Some actions to support my intention: ____________

An affirmation to support my intention: ____________

One self-care step I will take today: ____________

One thing I am looking forward to today: ____________

One thing I am grateful for today: ____________

MINDFUL EVENING

date: ____________

Journal Practice: Listen

The best part of today: ____________________

The hardest part of today: ____________________

I'm proud of myself for: ____________________

Pause and take three deep breaths. Tune into yourself. What are the words you need to hear right now? Write them here: ____________________

Three things I am grateful for in this moment: ____________________

RELEASE, RESPOND, RECEIVE

Journal Practice

date: ________

Release: let everything out, write down whatever is on your mind

Respond: pause and connect with your wise self, respond to the things you've written above

Receive: list at least three things you are grateful for in the moment

RELEASE, RESPOND, RECEIVE

Journal Practice

date: ____________

Release: let everything out, write down whatever is on your mind

Respond: pause and connect with your wise self, respond to the things you've written above

Receive: list at least three things you are grateful for in the moment

Use this space to free write, draw, or collage.

Use this space to free write, draw, or collage.

Week 2

PRACTICE:

Pause and breathe. Place your hand on your heart and take three deep breaths. Check in with your mind and body. Just notice what is true for you in the moment. This is one of my go-to practices. I do this several times a day, most days. The combination of placing a hand on your body and breathing deeply is grounding. Simply noticing what is arising for you in the moment is a mindfulness practice that supports self-compassion.

JOURNAL PROMPTS:

How do you know when you are connected with your intuition? What does it feel like in your body when you are connected with your intuition?

MINDFUL MORNING

Journal Practice: Listen

date: ____________

My intention for today: ______________________

Some actions to support my intention: ______________________

An affirmation to support my intention: ______________________

One self-care step I will take today: ______________________

One thing I am looking forward to today: ______________________

One thing I am grateful for today: ______________________

MINDFUL EVENING

date: ________

Journal Practice: Listen

The best part of today: ________

The hardest part of today: ________

I'm proud of myself for: ________

Pause and take three deep breaths. Tune into yourself. What are the words you need to hear right now? Write them here: ________

Three things I am grateful for in this moment: ________

RELEASE, RESPOND, RECEIVE

Journal Practice

date: ______________

Release: let everything out, write down whatever is on your mind

Respond: pause and connect with your wise self, respond to the things you've written above

Receive: list at least three things you are grateful for in the moment

RELEASE, RESPOND, RECEIVE

Journal Practice

date: ____________

Release: let everything out, write down whatever is on your mind

Respond: pause and connect with your wise self, respond to the things you've written above

Receive: list at least three things you are grateful for in the moment

MINDFUL MORNING

Journal Practice: Listen

date: ___________

My intention for today: ___________

Some actions to support my intention: ___________

An affirmation to support my intention: ___________

One self-care step I will take today: ___________

One thing I am looking forward to today: ___________

One thing I am grateful for today: ___________

MINDFUL EVENING

date: ____________

Journal Practice: Listen

The best part of today: ______________________________

____

____

____

The hardest part of today: ______________________________

____

____

____

I'm proud of myself for: ______________________________

____

____

____

Pause and take three deep breaths. Tune into yourself. What are the words you need to hear right now? Write them here: ______________

____

____

____

____

____

Three things I am grateful for in this moment: ______________

____

____

____

____

RELEASE, RESPOND, RECEIVE

Journal Practice

date: ____________

Release: let everything out, write down whatever is on your mind

Respond: pause and connect with your wise self, respond to the things you've written above

Receive: list at least three things you are grateful for in the moment

RELEASE, RESPOND, RECEIVE

Journal Practice

date: ____________

Release: let everything out, write down whatever is on your mind

Respond: pause and connect with your wise self, respond to the things you've written above

Receive: list at least three things you are grateful for in the moment

YOU
CAN

TRUST YOUR SELF.

Week 3

PRACTICE:

Listen to yourself first. Many people wake up and reach for their phone. Try starting your day connecting with yourself, hearing your own thoughts and feelings before you begin taking in other people's words and experiences.

JOURNAL PROMPTS:

What gets in the way of you connecting with your intuition?

What hinders you from living from your intuition? Are there any fears that arise as you think about allowing your wise inner self to guide your life?

MINDFUL MORNING

Journal Practice: Listen

date: ____________

My intention for today: ____________________

Some actions to support my intention: ____________________

An affirmation to support my intention: ____________________

One self-care step I will take today: ____________________

One thing I am looking forward to today: ____________________

One thing I am grateful for today: ____________________

MINDFUL EVENING

date: ____________

Journal Practice: Listen

The best part of today: ____________________

____

____

____

The hardest part of today: ____________________

____

____

____

I'm proud of myself for: ____________________

____

____

____

Pause and take three deep breaths. Tune into yourself. What are the words you need to hear right now? Write them here: ____________

____

____

____

____

____

Three things I am grateful for in this moment: ____________

____

____

____

____

RELEASE, RESPOND, RECEIVE

Journal Practice

date: ____________

Release: let everything out, write down whatever is on your mind

Respond: pause and connect with your wise self, respond to the things you've written above

Receive: list at least three things you are grateful for in the moment

RELEASE, RESPOND, RECEIVE

Journal Practice

date: ____________

Release: let everything out, write down whatever is on your mind

Respond: pause and connect with your wise self, respond to the things you've written above

Receive: list at least three things you are grateful for in the moment

MINDFUL MORNING

Journal Practice: Listen

date: ____________

My intention for today: ____________________

Some actions to support my intention: ____________________

An affirmation to support my intention: ____________________

One self-care step I will take today: ____________________

One thing I am looking forward to today: ____________________

One thing I am grateful for today: ____________________

MINDFUL EVENING

date: ______

Journal Practice: Listen

The best part of today: ______

The hardest part of today: ______

I'm proud of myself for: ______

Pause and take three deep breaths. Tune into yourself. What are the words you need to hear right now? Write them here: ______

Three things I am grateful for in this moment: ______

RELEASE, RESPOND, RECEIVE

Journal Practice

date: ___________

Release: let everything out, write down whatever is on your mind

Respond: pause and connect with your wise self, respond to the things you've written above

Receive: list at least three things you are grateful for in the moment

RELEASE, RESPOND, RECEIVE

Journal Practice

date: ____________

Release: let everything out, write down whatever is on your mind

Respond: pause and connect with your wise self, respond to the things you've written above

Receive: list at least three things you are grateful for in the moment

Use this space to free write, draw, or collage.

Use this space to free write, draw, or collage.

Week 4

PRACTICE:

Try Meditation. Meditation is one of my favorite ways to turn inward and connect with myself. Sometimes people believe the point of meditation is to clear your mind but what I've learned from my years of practicing is that meditation is about shifting the way you relate to your thoughts and feelings. Meditation is an opportunity to step back and witness what is arising within you *without any judgment*. Meditation is the practice of directing your attention. Some practices focus on the breath while others focus on a mantra or a feeling such as loving-kindness. I recommend starting with a guided practice if you are new to meditation. There are several resources listed at the end of this chapter.

JOURNAL PROMPTS:

What does your inner self want you to know?

Think of a time when you were guided by your intuition. What happened? How did it feel to listen to your wise inner knowing?

MINDFUL MORNING

Journal Practice: Listen

date: ______

My intention for today: ______

Some actions to support my intention: ______

An affirmation to support my intention: ______

One self-care step I will take today: ______

One thing I am looking forward to today: ______

One thing I am grateful for today: ______

MINDFUL EVENING

date: ________

Journal Practice: Listen

The best part of today: ______________________________

____

____

____

The hardest part of today: ______________________________

____

____

____

I'm proud of myself for: ______________________________

____

____

____

Pause and take three deep breaths. Tune into yourself. What are the words you need to hear right now? Write them here: ______________

____

____

____

____

____

Three things I am grateful for in this moment: ______________

____

____

____

____

RELEASE, RESPOND, RECEIVE

Journal Practice

date: ___________

Release: let everything out, write down whatever is on your mind

Respond: pause and connect with your wise self, respond to the things you've written above

Receive: list at least three things you are grateful for in the moment

RELEASE, RESPOND, RECEIVE

Journal Practice

date: ____________

Release: let everything out, write down whatever is on your mind

Respond: pause and connect with your wise self, respond to the things you've written above

Receive: list at least three things you are grateful for in the moment

MINDFUL MORNING

Journal Practice: Listen

date: ____________

My intention for today: ____

____

____

____

Some actions to support my intention: ________________________________

____

____

____

An affirmation to support my intention: ______________________________

____

____

____

One self-care step I will take today: ________________________________

____

____

____

One thing I am looking forward to today: _____________________________

____

____

____

One thing I am grateful for today: __________________________________

____

____

MINDFUL EVENING

date: ____________

Journal Practice: Listen

The best part of today: ______________________________

The hardest part of today: ______________________________

I'm proud of myself for: ______________________________

Pause and take three deep breaths. Tune into yourself. What are the words you need to hear right now? Write them here: ______________________________

Three things I am grateful for in this moment: ______________________________

RELEASE, RESPOND, RECEIVE

Journal Practice

date: ____________

Release: let everything out, write down whatever is on your mind

Respond: pause and connect with your wise self, respond to the things you've written above

Receive: list at least three things you are grateful for in the moment

RELEASE, RESPOND, RECEIVE

Journal Practice

date: ____________

Release: let everything out, write down whatever is on your mind

Respond: pause and connect with your wise self, respond to the things you've written above

Receive: list at least three things you are grateful for in the moment

Keep track of the days you complete a self-care practice by making a mark in the chart below. Let go of any perfectionism and instead allow this chart to be a celebration of the time and energy you are putting toward your Badass Self-Care practices.

	Journal writing	Meditation	Do Nothing	Pause & breathe	Other listening practice
1	○	○	○	○	○
2	○	○	○	○	○
3	○	○	○	○	○
4	○	○	○	○	○
5	○	○	○	○	○
6	○	○	○	○	○
7	○	○	○	○	○
8	○	○	○	○	○
9	○	○	○	○	○
10	○	○	○	○	○
11	○	○	○	○	○
12	○	○	○	○	○
13	○	○	○	○	○
14	○	○	○	○	○
15	○	○	○	○	○
16	○	○	○	○	○
17	○	○	○	○	○
18	○	○	○	○	○
19	○	○	○	○	○
20	○	○	○	○	○
21	○	○	○	○	○
22	○	○	○	○	○
23	○	○	○	○	○
24	○	○	○	○	○
25	○	○	○	○	○
26	○	○	○	○	○
27	○	○	○	○	○
28	○	○	○	○	○
29	○	○	○	○	○
30	○	○	○	○	○
31	○	○	○	○	○

Things I noticed this month….

FURTHER RESOURCES

Meditation Apps: Insight Timer, Headspace, and Calm
Journey to the Heart by Melody Beattie
The Artist's Way by Julia Cameron
My Sacred Pause by Melinda Scime
Outrageous Openness by Tosha Silver

CHAPTER TWO

Ground

The second component of Badass Self-Care is **Ground**. **Ground** is the practice of cultivating a loving relationship with our bodies. There are many layers to this practice: physically caring for the body, unpacking the messages we have received about bodies, and strengthening our connection with the body. I believe being in a human body is a gift. Our bodies are the vessels that allow our souls to be here on Earth and they deserve beautiful care. Also, because intuition lives in the body, tending to our bodies allows us to strengthen our relationship with our intuition.

Let's begin our journey with **Ground** by considering how we care for our bodies. Physically caring for our bodies includes nourishing ourselves with water, food, movement, and rest. In an ideal world, we would intuitively care for our bodies by drinking water when we are thirsty, eating when we are hungry, moving in a way that feels good for our bodies, and resting when we are tired. For most people, modern daily life does not allow time and space to respond intuitively to the body's needs. This month's practices and prompts will encourage you to explore your relationship with physically caring for your body inside the reality of your daily life.

We can't talk about cultivating a loving relationship with our bodies without talking about what *interferes* with us doing so. The systems we live inside of – namely, patriarchy, diet culture, white supremacy, and capitalism — create harmful hierarchies of bodies. As a result, the message we receive is that there is one "right" way to have a "good" body. It is beyond the scope of this book to detail the many ways these systems impact our relationship with our body but I want to briefly discuss patriarchy and diet culture in the spirit of beginning to build awareness. I highly recommend Sonya Renee Taylor's book, *The Body is Not an Apology*, for a deeper dive into the subject.

Patriarchy is a social system wherein men control the power and resources; it holds men and all things masculine as superior and denigrates women. Patriarchy teaches us that women are objects and our bodies are a thing to be presented to the world. Diet culture is directly related to patriarchy. Diet culture is a system of belief that values thinness, promotes weight loss, and equates body size with health. It feeds us lies about the importance of shrinking our bodies. Together, patriarchy and diet culture teach us to obsess over our bodies and how they look. We are made to believe that our appearance is the most important thing about us. This all plays right into the goal of patriarchy because it keeps us focused on striving toward an unrealistic beauty ideal rather than addressing the many ways we are being oppressed by patriarchy. Basically, if you are obsessed with losing weight you don't have time or energy to notice social issues like the wage gap or how women are not equally represented in our government.

Like many women, I spent years dissatisfied with my body. I had internalized the beliefs of patriarchy and diet culture. I saw my body as a representation of my worth and bought into the thin ideal. I hated my body and punished it accordingly with diets and exercise. Every Monday brought a new promise to "do better" which really just meant restricting and controlling my body. I prized productivity and achievement above all else and at any cost to my body. I did not listen to or honor my body's needs. I abused my body with substances and lack of rest. When I got sick and was forced to take time to heal, I would be frustrated with my body for letting me down.

Opting out of these systems takes work. Patriarchal diet culture messaging is ubiquitous. We have to *actively* work to unlearn and de-condition ourselves from this sociocultural programming. It is a practice of awareness of the messaging, understanding its impact on our culture as a whole and yourself as an individual, and choosing a different set of beliefs and behaviors. The practices and prompts in this chapter will help you unpack these messages and begin to choose a new way of relating to your body, one based on love and appreciation.

It took me many years of active work to shift my relationship with my body. I began unpacking patriarchal diet culture messaging when I was 25 years old and studying eating disorders in graduate school. I woke up to the reality of having a woman's body in this culture. I decided to opt out of the nonsense — to let go of the belief that my weight or size had anything to do with my worth as a person. I made a conscious choice to put my time, energy, and money toward changing the world rather than my waistline.

Even after decades of work, I still occasionally have negative thoughts about my body. I believe this is simply a symptom of the systems that we live in. When a negative thought about my body arises, I name it for what it is (internalized patriarchal diet culture nonsense) and then let it go. I don't grab on and follow the train of thought and I do not allow those negative thoughts to dictate my behavior. I make choices about my body from a place of self-love and body appreciation.

I am inviting you to opt out of this bullshit messaging and to shift your perspective about your body. I want you to know that your body and appearance are only one small piece of who you are as a person. I invite you to let go of over-focusing on your body and how you look. My hope is that you will learn to recognize how the systems we live inside of impact your views of your body so that you can choose a different way of being in relationship to your body — a way based on love and appreciation. Naming and critically examining our beliefs about bodies is a crucial step in cultivating a loving relationship with our own body.

The final piece of **Ground** is connecting with the wisdom of our bodies through embodiment. Embodiment is the state of being in our bodies. Of course, as long as you are alive you are in your body but are you really *in* your body? Our bodies speak to us through their own unique language of sensations. A tingling in our gut tells us we are excited about a connection with a new business partner. A tightness in our chest lets us know that we've just said yes to something we don't really want to do. Learning to connect with what you are feeling in your body – tension, relaxation, expansion, contraction, lightness, heaviness, tingling, warmth, shaking, buzzing, prickling – has the power to help you connect more deeply with your truth.

There is great wisdom in the sensations felt in the body but often we are not tuned into our body's messages. Many of us live our lives from the neck up. We are in our heads and disconnected from our bodies. Oftentimes, this is simply because of the nature of modern daily life. As a society, we are hyper-focused on thinking, planning, and analyzing. These are important skills and I am not suggesting that we stop using our minds, only that we also begin to invite in the wisdom of the body. This month we will explore practices and prompts for deepening your awareness of your body's messages.

Cultivating a loving relationship with your body is powerful work. This month's prompts and practices will provide you with a framework for taking beautiful care of your body, naming and letting go of harmful beliefs about your body, and deepening your relationship with your body and its felt sense. Let's get started.

Week 1

PRACTICE:

Stay hydrated. Drinking water is a simple and effective way to care for your body. Aim to drink at least 64 oz of water every day. If drinking water feels like a struggle, try sparkling water or adding fruit to your water. As you focus on staying hydrated, take note of the impact on your energy, concentration, and mood. If you'd like to, you can track your progress in the chart at the end of this chapter.

Say no to diet culture. Let go of trying to change your body and shift into a self-care mindset around food and movement. Despite what we have all been taught, there is no right or wrong when it comes to nourishing your body. There are no good or bad foods. Allow yourself to eat intuitively. Move your body in ways that are accessible to you and feel good. Shift your thoughts about movement away from burning calories and trying to change your body to finding joy in movement and celebrating your body.

JOURNAL PROMPTS:

How connected do you feel to your body's needs?

What is your current relationship with food? As you write, release any judgment or expectations. Allow yourself to just notice whatever arises in response to this prompt.

What if you surrendered the fight with your body? If you chose to love and accept yourself exactly as you are in this moment? How would this impact your relationship with food?

Shifting from the beliefs of diet culture and trying to change our bodies into acceptance and appreciation of our bodies can bring up some fear. What is your biggest fear when you consider making this change?

MINDFUL MORNING

Journal Practice: Ground

date: ________

This morning my body feels…

Today I will be kind to my body by…

Today my body needs…

An affirmation to support a loving relationship with my body:

MINDFUL EVENING

date: ____________

Journal Practice: Ground

Allow yourself to observe without judgment and rate your relationship today to the following aspects of physical self-care from 1 (lowest) to 10 (highest):

Hydration ____________ Food ____________

Movement ____________ Rest ____________

Today I cared for my body by:

Today I want to thank my body for:

RELEASE, RESPOND, RECEIVE

Journal Practice

date: ______

Release: let everything out, write down whatever is on your mind

Respond: pause and connect with your wise self, respond to the things you've written above

Receive: list at least three things you are grateful for in the moment

RELEASE, RESPOND, RECEIVE

Journal Practice

date: ______________

Release: let everything out, write down whatever is on your mind

Respond: pause and connect with your wise self, respond to the things you've written above

Receive: list at least three things you are grateful for in the moment

MINDFUL MORNING

Journal Practice: Ground

date: ____________

This morning my body feels...

Today I will be kind to my body by...

Today my body needs...

An affirmation to support a loving relationship with my body:

MINDFUL EVENING

date: ____________

Journal Practice: Ground

Allow yourself to observe without judgment and rate your relationship today to the following aspects of physical self-care from 1 (lowest) to 10 (highest):

Hydration ____________________

Food ____________________

Movement ____________________

Rest ____________________

Today I cared for my body by:

Today I want to thank my body for:

RELEASE, RESPOND, RECEIVE

Journal Practice

date: ____________

Release: let everything out, write down whatever is on your mind

Respond: pause and connect with your wise self, respond to the things you've written above

Receive: list at least three things you are grateful for in the moment

RELEASE, RESPOND, RECEIVE

Journal Practice

date: ________

Release: let everything out, write down whatever is on your mind

Respond: pause and connect with your wise self, respond to the things you've written above

Receive: list at least three things you are grateful for in the moment

Use this space to free write, draw, or collage.

Use this space to free write, draw, or collage.

Week 2

PRACTICE:

Rest. Rest is about so much more than getting a good night's sleep. Rest includes taking breaks physically, mentally, and emotionally. Trying to be consistently alert and productive is how we burn out. Rest is essential. What feels like rest for you? This week experiment with resting for a few minutes every day. This could mean taking a nap, spending a few quiet minutes alone, or taking a break from technology.

Make pleasure a priority. Our bodies are designed for pleasure. What feels good in your body? I find it helpful to keep the five senses in mind. What sights, smells, sounds, tastes, and sensations bring you pleasure? Some ideas include burning incense or lighting a candle, taking a hot shower or bath, picking or buying fresh flowers for your table or altar, dancing to your favorite song, putting your bare feet on the earth, and drinking hot herbal tea or cold sparkling water. Commit to a simple act of pleasure every day this week.

JOURNAL PROMPTS:

What does rest mean to you?

What comes up when you think about consciously choosing to incorporate more rest into your life? Where might your ideas about resting come from?

How can you include more rest in your day, week, month? Be specific.

What is your current relationship to pleasure?

Make a list of things that bring you pleasure. Keep in mind your five senses. What sights, sounds, smells, taste, and sensations bring you pleasure?

MINDFUL MORNING

date:

Journal Practice: Ground

This morning my body feels…

Today I will be kind to my body by…

Today my body needs…

An affirmation to support a loving relationship with my body:

MINDFUL EVENING

date: ____________

Journal Practice: Ground

Allow yourself to observe without judgment and rate your relationship today to the following aspects of physical self-care from 1 (lowest) to 10 (highest):

Hydration ____________________ Food ____________________

Movement ____________________ Rest ____________________

Today I cared for my body by:

____

____

____

____

____

____

____

Today I want to thank my body for:

____

____

____

____

____

____

____

RELEASE, RESPOND, RECEIVE

Journal Practice

date: __________

Release: let everything out, write down whatever is on your mind

Respond: pause and connect with your wise self, respond to the things you've written above

Receive: list at least three things you are grateful for in the moment

RELEASE, RESPOND, RECEIVE

Journal Practice

date: ____________

Release: let everything out, write down whatever is on your mind

Respond: pause and connect with your wise self, respond to the things you've written above

Receive: list at least three things you are grateful for in the moment

MINDFUL MORNING

Journal Practice: Ground

date: ____________

This morning my body feels…

Today I will be kind to my body by…

Today my body needs…

An affirmation to support a loving relationship with my body:

MINDFUL EVENING

date: ____________

Journal Practice: Ground

Allow yourself to observe without judgment and rate your relationship today to the following aspects of physical self-care from 1 (lowest) to 10 (highest):

Hydration ____________ Food ____________

Movement ____________ Rest ____________

Today I cared for my body by:

Today I want to thank my body for:

RELEASE, RESPOND, RECEIVE

Journal Practice

date: ___________

Release: let everything out, write down whatever is on your mind

Respond: pause and connect with your wise self, respond to the things you've written above

Receive: list at least three things you are grateful for in the moment

RELEASE, RESPOND, RECEIVE

Journal Practice

date: ___________

Release: let everything out, write down whatever is on your mind

Respond: pause and connect with your wise self, respond to the things you've written above

Receive: list at least three things you are grateful for in the moment

YOU DIVINE

ARE
LOVE
EMBODIED.

Week 3

PRACTICE:

Technology Boundaries. Technology interferes with our ability to be connected to our bodies. This week I invite you to consider some boundaries around your technology use. This could mean having a designated "switch off" time where you don't use any technology (e.g., 9pm-8am) or a "no tech" area of your house (e.g., the dinner table or your bedroom) or leaving your phone behind during certain activities (e.g., while taking a walk or soaking in the bathtub).

Go outside. Spending time in nature brings me back into my body. This week I invite you to spend a few minutes outside every day. You could go out for a walk or even just step outside and look up at the sky for a few minutes. If you'd like to, you can track your progress in the chart at the end of this chapter.

JOURNAL PROMPTS:

What helps you be *in* your body?

A running list of what feels good in my body:

(consider people, places, activities, food, habits, and anything else that arises for you)

A running list of what does *not* feel good in my body:

(consider people, places, activities, food, habits, and anything else that arises for you)

MINDFUL MORNING

Journal Practice: Ground

date: ________

This morning my body feels…

Today I will be kind to my body by…

Today my body needs…

An affirmation to support a loving relationship with my body:

MINDFUL EVENING

date: ____________

Journal Practice: Ground

Allow yourself to observe without judgment and rate your relationship today to the following aspects of physical self-care from 1 (lowest) to 10 (highest):

Hydration ____________________ Food ____________________

Movement ____________________ Rest ____________________

Today I cared for my body by:

Today I want to thank my body for:

RELEASE, RESPOND, RECEIVE

Journal Practice

date: ____________

Release: let everything out, write down whatever is on your mind

Respond: pause and connect with your wise self, respond to the things you've written above

Receive: list at least three things you are grateful for in the moment

RELEASE, RESPOND, RECEIVE

Journal Practice

date: __________

Release: let everything out, write down whatever is on your mind

Respond: pause and connect with your wise self, respond to the things you've written above

Receive: list at least three things you are grateful for in the moment

MINDFUL MORNING

Journal Practice: Ground

date: ____________

This morning my body feels…

Today I will be kind to my body by…

Today my body needs…

An affirmation to support a loving relationship with my body:

MINDFUL EVENING

date: ____________

Journal Practice: Ground

Allow yourself to observe without judgment and rate your relationship today to the following aspects of physical self-care from 1 (lowest) to 10 (highest):

Hydration ____________________ Food ____________________

Movement ____________________ Rest ____________________

Today I cared for my body by:

____

____

____

____

____

____

____

Today I want to thank my body for:

____

____

____

____

____

____

____

RELEASE, RESPOND, RECEIVE

Journal Practice

date: ________

Release: let everything out, write down whatever is on your mind

Respond: pause and connect with your wise self, respond to the things you've written above

Receive: list at least three things you are grateful for in the moment

RELEASE, RESPOND, RECEIVE

Journal Practice

date: ____________

Release: let everything out, write down whatever is on your mind

Respond: pause and connect with your wise self, respond to the things you've written above

Receive: list at least three things you are grateful for in the moment

Use this space to free write, draw, or collage.

Use this space to free write, draw, or collage.

Week 4

PRACTICE:

Mindful check-in. Set four reminders during the day to check in with your body. For example, you might set an alarm on your phone for 10am, 1pm, 4pm, and 7pm. When the alarm goes off, simply pause and notice what your body needs. It's okay if you can't meet the need in the moment. Just noticing is a powerful practice.

Body Compass. Your body has a knowing that is beyond logical or rational thought. This exercise will help you begin to connect with your body's wisdom. Explore what a "no" feels like in your body. Think of a time when you felt out of alignment – perhaps you were in a job you didn't like or an unhealthy relationship or even just driving to a party you didn't want to attend. As you recall this time or moment, what do you feel in your body? Next, identify what a "yes" feels like in your body. Recall a time where you felt in alignment – like you were in the right place at the right time or doing something that you truly enjoyed. Think back on this moment and notice what you feel in your body. Be as specific as possible (e.g., "no" feels like tension in my shoulders and "yes" feels like tingling in my hands). This is your body compass, a concept I first learned about through the work of author Martha Beck. You now know what "no" and "yes" feel like in your body. As you go about your daily life, the sensations in your body may not feel as strong as what came up during this exercise but you can still use your body compass to help you make decisions big and small. If you're thinking of taking a new job, imagine yourself there and see how it feels in your body. When you're deciding where to go for dinner, observe how each option feels inside your body. Experiment with making decisions based on how they feel in your body. Practice connecting with the wisdom that lies within your cells and observe the impact on your life.

JOURNAL PROMPTS:

What interferes with you lovingly responding to your body? Consider time constraints, beliefs, lack of access to resources, and anything else that feels relevant.

What are your beliefs about your body? Where did they come from? Who benefits from you believing them? What would you like to believe instead?

In an ideal world, how would you care for your body? What would you do daily, monthly, weekly, yearly?

Dear Body, Please forgive me for...

Dear Body, Thank you for...

Dear Body, I promise...

MINDFUL MORNING

Journal Practice: Ground

date: ____________

This morning my body feels…

Today I will be kind to my body by…

Today my body needs…

An affirmation to support a loving relationship with my body:

MINDFUL EVENING

date: ______________

Journal Practice: Ground

Allow yourself to observe without judgment and rate your relationship today to the following aspects of physical self-care from 1 (lowest) to 10 (highest):

Hydration ______________ Food ______________

Movement ______________ Rest ______________

Today I cared for my body by:

Today I want to thank my body for:

RELEASE, RESPOND, RECEIVE

Journal Practice

date: ________

Release: let everything out, write down whatever is on your mind

Respond: pause and connect with your wise self, respond to the things you've written above

Receive: list at least three things you are grateful for in the moment

RELEASE, RESPOND, RECEIVE

Journal Practice

date: ____________

Release: let everything out, write down whatever is on your mind

Respond: pause and connect with your wise self, respond to the things you've written above

Receive: list at least three things you are grateful for in the moment

MINDFUL MORNING

Journal Practice: Ground

date: ____________

This morning my body feels…

Today I will be kind to my body by…

Today my body needs…

An affirmation to support a loving relationship with my body:

MINDFUL EVENING

date: ____________

Journal Practice: Ground

Allow yourself to observe without judgment and rate your relationship today to the following aspects of physical self-care from 1 (lowest) to 10 (highest):

Hydration ____________________

Food ____________________

Movement ____________________

Rest ____________________

Today I cared for my body by:

Today I want to thank my body for:

RELEASE, RESPOND, RECEIVE

Journal Practice

date: __________

Release: let everything out, write down whatever is on your mind

Respond: pause and connect with your wise self, respond to the things you've written above

Receive: list at least three things you are grateful for in the moment

RELEASE, RESPOND, RECEIVE

Journal Practice

date: ____________

Release: let everything out, write down whatever is on your mind

Respond: pause and connect with your wise self, respond to the things you've written above

Receive: list at least three things you are grateful for in the moment

Keep track of the days you complete a self-care practice by making a mark in the chart below. Let go of any perfectionism and instead allow this chart to be a celebration of the time and energy you are putting toward your Badass Self-Care practices.

	Journal writing	Meditation	64 oz of water	Technology boundaries	Go Outside	Other
1	○	○	○	○	○	○
2	○	○	○	○	○	○
3	○	○	○	○	○	○
4	○	○	○	○	○	○
5	○	○	○	○	○	○
6	○	○	○	○	○	○
7	○	○	○	○	○	○
8	○	○	○	○	○	○
9	○	○	○	○	○	○
10	○	○	○	○	○	○
11	○	○	○	○	○	○
12	○	○	○	○	○	○
13	○	○	○	○	○	○
14	○	○	○	○	○	○
15	○	○	○	○	○	○
16	○	○	○	○	○	○
17	○	○	○	○	○	○
18	○	○	○	○	○	○
19	○	○	○	○	○	○
20	○	○	○	○	○	○
21	○	○	○	○	○	○
22	○	○	○	○	○	○
23	○	○	○	○	○	○
24	○	○	○	○	○	○
25	○	○	○	○	○	○
26	○	○	○	○	○	○
27	○	○	○	○	○	○
28	○	○	○	○	○	○
29	○	○	○	○	○	○
30	○	○	○	○	○	○
31	○	○	○	○	○	○

Things I noticed this month....

FURTHER RESOURCES

The Body is Not an Apology by Sonya Renee Taylor
Intuitive Eating by Evelyn Tribole
Health at Every Size by Linda Bacon
Being in Your Body by Fariha Roisin
The Fuck It Diet by Caroline Dooner
How to Break Up with Your Phone by Catherine Price

CHAPTER THREE

Release

The third component of Badass Self-Care is **Release**. **Release** is the practice of letting go of what no longer serves us. This month we will explore our relationship with our outer and inner worlds, including our belongings, beliefs, and habits. We will also consider practices for releasing our emotions and cleansing our energy. The practices of **Listen** and **Ground** have helped you to form a deeper connection with your inner self and the wisdom of your body. We approach this practice of **Release** from the foundation of **Listen** and **Ground** so that we can choose what to let go of based on our inner truth and wisdom, rather than other people's ideas or expectations. Letting go of what no longer feels aligned allows us to create room for new things to enter our world.

The first step of **Release** is to notice how things are feeling inside of your life. We begin by simply gathering information and building our awareness. Next, we identify what is most important to us, our top priorities. The truth is we can't do it all. Getting clear about our priorities helps us decide what we want to give our time and energy to, as well as what we are ready to let go of. Then, we begin the process of releasing belongings, beliefs, and habits that no longer feel in alignment. This month's practices and prompts will guide you through these steps.

There is a lot in life that we cannot control. We have the power to choose where we put our attention. If we choose to focus on things that are out of our hands, we will feel overwhelmed and helpless, maybe even stuck and sad. If we choose to focus on what is within our control, we will feel more capable and hopeful, maybe even empowered and calm. Part of the mental and emotional work of **Release** is focusing on what we can control and letting go of the rest. This month I hope to encourage and empower you to make changes where you can.

One place where we have the power to enact change is our physical environment. Our surroundings impact us emotionally and energetically. The things that we are surrounded by can create feelings of chaos or help us feel calm and grounded. Taking the time to observe how you feel in your home and around your belongings will help you discern what you are ready to release. We each get to create our own criteria for whether something stays or goes. Marie Kondo famously instructs people to hold items in their hands and see if they spark joy. Others tell us to ask if something is useful or beautiful. Working from your own inner authority, this month you will decide what belongings you are ready to release.

Our minds are another area of our lives where we have the power to create change. Moving from our outer to inner world, we begin by bringing awareness to our thoughts. What we think and believe has a powerful influence in our lives. We have a constant stream of thoughts going through our minds, but most of us are not aware of what we are saying to ourselves as we go about our days. Research shows that 80% of our thoughts are negative and 95% of our thoughts we have had before. This means we think the same, mostly negative, thoughts day after day. Our thoughts and beliefs are powerful because they impact our feelings and behavior.

Let's use the example of taking time for self-care. If I believe taking time for myself is selfish, I might have thoughts like, "I shouldn't be doing this" or "I'm a bad mom." These thoughts will lead to me feeling guilty and anxious. They could impact my behavior in several ways; I might over-function in my roles or struggle to set boundaries. Conversely, if I believe that taking time for myself is essential and that I am worthy of care, my thoughts might include "I deserve care" or "Taking time for self-care allows me to show up in the world as the best version of myself." These thoughts will lead to me feeling empowered and calm. They too could impact my behavior in several ways; I might take time for myself more regularly or more easily set boundaries. Actively working with our thoughts and beliefs can create powerful changes in our lives.

The first step toward changing our thoughts and beliefs is awareness. Meditation and journal writing are two wonderful tools for building awareness of our thoughts. If you have gotten away from these practices, now is a great time to recommit. We can always begin again and I invite you to do so from a place of curiosity and compassion. Remember that even a few minutes of practice can have a powerful impact.

Once we've built awareness of our thoughts and beliefs then we can begin to work toward change from a place of self-compassion. Because our thoughts impact our feelings and behaviors, changing our thoughts alters our feelings and behaviors, and ultimately our lives. Shifting our thoughts and beliefs is powerful, but it takes work. When releasing old thoughts and beliefs it is helpful to create new ideas to replace the ones we are letting go of. Once we have articulated new thoughts, we need to *actively* work with them. You can do this by writing or saying them daily, putting them on sticky notes around the house, programming them into your phone as reminders to pop up throughout the day, or creating a piece of art around them. Replacing old thoughts and beliefs takes regular effort. Many of our default thoughts are automatic and have been with us for a very long time. They aren't simply going to shift or go away. We have to put in the work to change them.

This month I will also invite you to consider your habits and decide if there are any areas where you'd like to make adjustments. A habit is anything you do repeatedly and regularly. What behaviors make up your daily life? Do they feel nourishing? Are they congruent with your priorities? As always, come back to your inner authority to discern what feels aligned for you in this moment. We are ever-evolving creatures, and you are allowed to change your mind. I invite you to be especially mindful of habits around substance use and technology, as well as behaviors like complaining or gossiping. Be kind *and* be honest with yourself.

This month's prompts will help you identify what habits you want to start or continue as well as any habits you are ready to let go of.

Lastly, the practice of **Release** is also about emotionally and energetically letting go. What helps you to express your emotions and cleanse your energy? Some ideas include crying, writing, going to therapy, talking to a trusted person, moving your body, meditating, taking an Epsom salt bath, spending time in nature, and working with an energy healer. This chapter includes several practices and prompts to support the development of healthy emotional and energetic releasing.

I am continuously engaged in the practices of **Release**. Like many people, it feels like I am always working to clear the clutter from my home. I've learned to enjoy the process of sorting and organizing my belongings. I light a candle, put on a podcast or playlist, and do the work of decluttering in the spirit of self-love. I am now able to find joy in letting go of things. I am also more mindful about what I buy, and I try to stay connected to my intention of creating a beautiful and orderly home environment when making decisions about purchases.

Beyond the practice of letting go of literal stuff, I continue to work with releasing beliefs and habits that no longer serve me. This work has been especially powerful for me when it comes to acknowledging and taking care of my own needs. In my mid-thirties, I learned about the Highly Sensitive Person (HSP) and it changed my life. HSPs have increased emotional sensitivity and stronger reactions to external and internal stimuli. In short, we feel things a lot! Learning that I am an HSP helped me understand why I felt so deeply affected by many things that seemed to just roll right off of other people. Before learning about HSPs, I thought there was something wrong with me and that I needed to change – to toughen up, to not be so emotional. Now I understand that my sensitivity is a gift and I deserve care, even if my needs are different or more involved.

I require a lot of self-care in order to show up in my life as the person I want to be, and I have let go of feeling guilty about it. Regularly taking time to release my emotions and reset my energy allows me to be present, grounded, and compassionate with my loved ones and clients. My current self-care routine includes writing in my journal every morning, taking a daily walk by myself, soaking in the bathtub a few times a week, and going to therapy at least once a month. I also use meditation, breathing practices, and essential oils for grounding throughout the day. I don't see my self-care time as selfish; I truly see it as being of service to myself and others.

This month's practices and prompts will help you bring more awareness to your outer and inner world so that you can notice what feels out of alignment and begin letting go of what no longer serves you. You will also explore practices for emotional and energetic releasing. The work of **Release** prepares us for the next two components of Badass Self Care, **Speak** and **Act**, by helping us create space in our lives so that we can name our dreams and begin taking steps toward them.

Week 1

PRACTICE:

Clear one small space. Let's begin our releasing practice with something physical. Set yourself up for success and choose a space that feels doable. Pick something that you can clear and organize in 30 minutes or less. This could be your nightstand, purse, or kitchen counter. Notice how you feel on the inside after creating some order on the outside.

Take a walk. Moving your body is a wonderful way to invite in some release. There are several physical and emotional benefits to physical activity. If walking is not accessible to you, feel free to choose any type of movement that feels supportive. This week aim to take a walk (or do another type of movement) every day, even if only for five minutes. If it feels supportive for you, track the days you take a walk (or engage in other movement) in the chart at the end of this chapter.

JOURNAL PROMPTS:

How do you want to feel inside of your life?

What are you surrounded by in your daily life? How does it make you feel?

What do you notice in your body when you look in your closet?

How is the energy in your home environment (and any other places you spend a lot of time)? What feels good? What are you ready to release?

Let's begin this month by simply observing. Notice how you feel around the people you interact with, at the places you go, and during the activities that make up your days. Gather information on what feels aligned for you and what doesn't. This will help you decide what you are ready to release.

Things that no longer feel aligned for me:

MINDFUL MORNING

Journal Practice: Release

date: ______

Today I will practice tuning into my inner wise self by:

Today I want to feel:

One thing I will do to create this feeling:

One thing I will *not* do to help create this feeling:

An affirmation to support the way I want to feel:

MINDFUL EVENING

date: ____________

Journal Practice: Release

Things that felt aligned for me today (people, places, activities):

Things that did not feel aligned for me today (people, places, activities):

I'm ready to let go of:

Three things I am grateful for in this moment:

RELEASE, RESPOND, RECEIVE

Journal Practice

date: ___________

Release: let everything out, write down whatever is on your mind

Respond: pause and connect with your wise self, respond to the things you've written above

Receive: list at least three things you are grateful for in the moment

RELEASE, RESPOND, RECEIVE

Journal Practice

date: ____________

Release: let everything out, write down whatever is on your mind

Respond: pause and connect with your wise self, respond to the things you've written above

Receive: list at least three things you are grateful for in the moment

MINDFUL MORNING

Journal Practice: Release

date: ________

Today I will practice tuning into my inner wise self by:

Today I want to feel:

One thing I will do to create this feeling:

One thing I will *not* do to help create this feeling:

An affirmation to support the way I want to feel:

MINDFUL EVENING

date: ____________

Journal Practice: Release

Things that felt aligned for me today (people, places, activities):

Things that did not feel aligned for me today (people, places, activities):

I'm ready to let go of:

Three things I am grateful for in this moment:

RELEASE, RESPOND, RECEIVE

Journal Practice

date: ____________

Release: let everything out, write down whatever is on your mind

Respond: pause and connect with your wise self, respond to the things you've written above

Receive: list at least three things you are grateful for in the moment

RELEASE, RESPOND, RECEIVE

Journal Practice

date: ____________

Release: let everything out, write down whatever is on your mind

Respond: pause and connect with your wise self, respond to the things you've written above

Receive: list at least three things you are grateful for in the moment

Use this space to free write, draw, or collage.

Use this space to free write, draw, or collage.

Week 2

PRACTICE:

Name your priorities. What is most important to you? Try to narrow it down to three priorities. There are no right or wrong answers here. Your priorities might be self-care, service, and family or creativity, joy, and compassion or love, health, and abundance or career, spirituality, and freedom. After you have identified your priorities, compare them with how you spend your time by taking a look at your calendar and to-do list. If you identified family as a priority, how much time are you spending with family? If you noted creativity as a priority, how much space are you devoting to creative endeavors? For now, just notice where things feel out of alignment.

JOURNAL PROMPTS:

How are you spending your time and energy? Is it congruent with your priorities?

Where do things feel out of alignment? What can you shift or release to bring things into alignment?

What thoughts do you notice yourself having over and over?

What thoughts are you ready to let go of?

MINDFUL MORNING

Journal Practice: Release

date: ________

Today I will practice tuning into my inner wise self by:

Today I want to feel:

One thing I will do to create this feeling:

One thing I will *not* do to help create this feeling:

An affirmation to support the way I want to feel:

MINDFUL EVENING

date: ____________

Journal Practice: Release

Things that felt aligned for me today (people, places, activities):

Things that did not feel aligned for me today (people, places, activities):

I'm ready to let go of:

Three things I am grateful for in this moment:

RELEASE, RESPOND, RECEIVE

Journal Practice

date: ____________

Release: let everything out, write down whatever is on your mind

Respond: pause and connect with your wise self, respond to the things you've written above

Receive: list at least three things you are grateful for in the moment

RELEASE, RESPOND, RECEIVE

Journal Practice

date: ____________

Release: let everything out, write down whatever is on your mind

Respond: pause and connect with your wise self, respond to the things you've written above

Receive: list at least three things you are grateful for in the moment

MINDFUL MORNING

Journal Practice: Release

date: ___________

Today I will practice tuning into my inner wise self by:

Today I want to feel:

One thing I will do to create this feeling:

One thing I will *not* do to help create this feeling:

An affirmation to support the way I want to feel:

MINDFUL EVENING

Journal Practice: Release

date: __________

Things that felt aligned for me today (people, places, activities):

Things that did not feel aligned for me today (people, places, activities):

I'm ready to let go of:

Three things I am grateful for in this moment:

RELEASE, RESPOND, RECEIVE

Journal Practice

date: ____________

Release: let everything out, write down whatever is on your mind

Respond: pause and connect with your wise self, respond to the things you've written above

Receive: list at least three things you are grateful for in the moment

RELEASE, RESPOND, RECEIVE

Journal Practice

date: ___________

Release: let everything out, write down whatever is on your mind

Respond: pause and connect with your wise self, respond to the things you've written above

Receive: list at least three things you are grateful for in the moment

YOU

ENO

ARE

UGH.

Week 3

PRACTICE:

Breath Work. Our breath is a powerful tool for physical and emotional release. There are many types of breathing practices and I've included some further resources on the topic at the end of this chapter. For this week, I invite you to work with a simple conscious breathing practice that focuses on the exhale. Begin by coming into a comfortable seated position. Just notice your natural breath for a few moments. Then begin the practice of 4-7-8 breath by breathing in for a count of four, holding your breath for a count of seven, and exhaling through your mouth for a count of eight. Continue for three to five minutes. If you become uncomfortable at any time, return to your natural breath. If it feels supportive, track your breath work practice in the chart at the end of the chapter.

Old Story, New Story. Identify an old story that you would like to shift or release. This might be a belief about yourself, others, or the world. Once you've identified the story you'd like to work with, write it out in detail. Next, think about what you would like to believe instead and write a new story. It's important not to bullshit yourself during this practice. Write something that feels at least a little bit true. I find it helpful to add the words "I'm learning" if it's hard to believe something new. Re-read your new story every day, maybe even several times a day.

JOURNAL PROMPTS:

What beliefs do you hold about yourself, others, or the world that are no longer serving you?

What would you like to believe instead?

Consider the behaviors that make up your daily life. What habits restore you and feel good emotionally and energetically? What habits do you want to continue? Is there a new habit you'd like to incorporate into your life?

What habits feel draining? What habits are you ready to let go of?

MINDFUL MORNING

Journal Practice: Release

date: ____________

Today I will practice tuning into my inner wise self by:

Today I want to feel:

One thing I will do to create this feeling:

One thing I will *not* do to help create this feeling:

An affirmation to support the way I want to feel:

MINDFUL EVENING

date: ______

Journal Practice: Release

Things that felt aligned for me today (people, places, activities):

Things that did not feel aligned for me today (people, places, activities):

I'm ready to let go of:

Three things I am grateful for in this moment:

RELEASE, RESPOND, RECEIVE

Journal Practice

date: ________

Release: let everything out, write down whatever is on your mind

Respond: pause and connect with your wise self, respond to the things you've written above

Receive: list at least three things you are grateful for in the moment

RELEASE, RESPOND, RECEIVE

Journal Practice

date: ____________

Release: let everything out, write down whatever is on your mind

Respond: pause and connect with your wise self, respond to the things you've written above

Receive: list at least three things you are grateful for in the moment

MINDFUL MORNING

date: ____________

Journal Practice: Release

Today I will practice tuning into my inner wise self by:

Today I want to feel:

One thing I will do to create this feeling:

One thing I will *not* do to help create this feeling:

An affirmation to support the way I want to feel:

MINDFUL EVENING

date: ______

Journal Practice: Release

Things that felt aligned for me today (people, places, activities):

Things that did not feel aligned for me today (people, places, activities):

I'm ready to let go of:

Three things I am grateful for in this moment:

RELEASE, RESPOND, RECEIVE

Journal Practice

date: __________

Release: let everything out, write down whatever is on your mind

Respond: pause and connect with your wise self, respond to the things you've written above

Receive: list at least three things you are grateful for in the moment

RELEASE, RESPOND, RECEIVE

Journal Practice

date: __________

Release: let everything out, write down whatever is on your mind

Respond: pause and connect with your wise self, respond to the things you've written above

Receive: list at least three things you are grateful for in the moment

Use this space to free write, draw, or collage.

Use this space to free write, draw, or collage.

Week 4

PRACTICE:

Releasing Ceremony. Ground yourself with a few minutes of meditation or conscious breathing. Write down everything you want to release on a piece of paper. Fold up the paper and hold it close to your heart. State your intention to release what no longer serves you. If it resonates, ask for support from Spirit/ God/ The Universe. To complete the ceremony, rip up the paper and release it into the elements in some way. You could burn it in a fire, bury it in the earth, or release it into the wind or a body of water.

JOURNAL PROMPTS:

How do you hold space for your feelings? What practices do you want to incorporate into your life to help with releasing your emotions?

How do you reset or cleanse your energy?

What do you want to invite into your life?

What is preventing you from moving forward?

What are you ready to let go of?

MINDFUL MORNING

Journal Practice: Release

date: ____________

Today I will practice tuning into my inner wise self by:

Today I want to feel:

One thing I will do to create this feeling:

One thing I will *not* do to help create this feeling:

An affirmation to support the way I want to feel:

MINDFUL EVENING

date: ____________

Journal Practice: Release

Things that felt aligned for me today (people, places, activities):

Things that did not feel aligned for me today (people, places, activities):

I'm ready to let go of:

Three things I am grateful for in this moment:

RELEASE, RESPOND, RECEIVE

Journal Practice

date: ________

Release: let everything out, write down whatever is on your mind

Respond: pause and connect with your wise self, respond to the things you've written above

Receive: list at least three things you are grateful for in the moment

RELEASE, RESPOND, RECEIVE

Journal Practice

date: ____________

Release: let everything out, write down whatever is on your mind

Respond: pause and connect with your wise self, respond to the things you've written above

Receive: list at least three things you are grateful for in the moment

MINDFUL MORNING

Journal Practice: Release

date: ________

Today I will practice tuning into my inner wise self by:

Today I want to feel:

One thing I will do to create this feeling:

One thing I will *not* do to help create this feeling:

An affirmation to support the way I want to feel:

MINDFUL EVENING

date: __________

Journal Practice: Release

Things that felt aligned for me today (people, places, activities):

Things that did not feel aligned for me today (people, places, activities):

I'm ready to let go of:

Three things I am grateful for in this moment:

RELEASE, RESPOND, RECEIVE

Journal Practice

date: ________

Release: let everything out, write down whatever is on your mind

Respond: pause and connect with your wise self, respond to the things you've written above

Receive: list at least three things you are grateful for in the moment

RELEASE, RESPOND, RECEIVE

Journal Practice

date: ____________

Release: let everything out, write down whatever is on your mind

Respond: pause and connect with your wise self, respond to the things you've written above

Receive: list at least three things you are grateful for in the moment

Keep track of the days you complete a self-care practice by making a mark in the chart below. Let go of any perfectionism and instead allow this chart to be a celebration of the time and energy you are putting toward your Badass Self-Care practices.

	Journal writing	Meditation	Walking or other movement	Breath work	Other
1	○	○	○	○	○
2	○	○	○	○	○
3	○	○	○	○	○
4	○	○	○	○	○
5	○	○	○	○	○
6	○	○	○	○	○
7	○	○	○	○	○
8	○	○	○	○	○
9	○	○	○	○	○
10	○	○	○	○	○
11	○	○	○	○	○
12	○	○	○	○	○
13	○	○	○	○	○
14	○	○	○	○	○
15	○	○	○	○	○
16	○	○	○	○	○
17	○	○	○	○	○
18	○	○	○	○	○
19	○	○	○	○	○
20	○	○	○	○	○
21	○	○	○	○	○
22	○	○	○	○	○
23	○	○	○	○	○
24	○	○	○	○	○
25	○	○	○	○	○
26	○	○	○	○	○
27	○	○	○	○	○
28	○	○	○	○	○
29	○	○	○	○	○
30	○	○	○	○	○
31	○	○	○	○	○

Things I noticed this month...

FURTHER RESOURCES

The Highly Sensitive Person by Elaine N. Aron, Ph.D.
The Life Changing Magic of Tidying Up by Marie Kondo
How to Breathe by Ashley Neese
Conscious Communications by Mary Shores
The Breathing App

CHAPTER FOUR

Speak

The fourth component of Badass Self-Care is **Speak**. **Speak** is the practice of naming our desires and allowing ourselves to want. This month we will be identifying our hopes, dreams, and desires. I adore this part of the work; it can be so juicy and impactful! My own life changed drastically after I first let myself consider what I really wanted. As always, please approach these practices and prompts from a place of connection with your inner wise self. Many of us have spent years building our lives around a desire to please others and gain approval. **Speak** asks you to set aside other people's expectations and tune into your inner wise self so that you can name *your* true desires.

A lot of women have trouble answering the question, "What do *you* want?" We know what is expected of us. We know what other people want from us. But when it comes to what we want for ourselves, many of us feel unsure. Honestly, many women have not even bothered to consider what they want because they are so consumed with meeting the demands of society, work, family, and the many roles they play in their daily lives. The truth is we all have hopes, dreams, and desires. They may be buried underneath layers of responsibilities, fear, and expectations, but they are there inside of you waiting for your attention. *What you want matters.* You are a person in your *own* right. Give yourself permission to speak and give voice to your hopes, dreams, and desires.

The first step of **Speak** is to name any potential blocks that might interfere with us claiming what we want. We acknowledge the messages we have received about women and wanting. We name any fears that are arising as we think about allowing ourselves to dream. Giving voice to these messages and fears diminishes their power and clears the way for us to name our desires. Next, we allow ourselves to dream! We envision how things would look and feel if we were living our ideal lives. We consider what we want to do with our one wild and precious life and how we want to feel inside of it. Finally, we continue the process of taking stock that we began during **Release**. This allows us to make note of the space between where we currently are and where we want to be so that we can begin to take action in service of our hopes, dreams, and desires.

We begin the work of **Speak** by delving into any potential blocks, so that we can name our desires with mindful awareness and an open heart. Blocks are those things that interfere with us claiming what we want. Sometimes we don't allow ourselves to want because of the messages we have received about women and wanting. Patriarchy teaches us that women should serve others. It celebrates the notion of a selfless woman who puts herself last (especially when it comes to motherhood). We're taught that a "good woman" keeps herself "under control." She is not too emotional or loud. She stays small (in every sense of the word) and accepts that her desires do not matter. Patriarchy has always been afraid of women's wanting. We've been taught that our desires are bad, dangerous, and sinful. It's time to unpack this bullshit messaging and reclaim our desires.

Aside from the systemic messages we receive about women and wanting, sometimes we don't allow ourselves to want because we are afraid. We fear being too much or not enough. We are afraid of disappointing others. We are nervous about what people will think. We worry that if we start to change, we will lose friends or be judged by our family. Taking the time to acknowledge our fears diminishes their power.

One major fear that holds women back from naming their dreams is perfectionism. You may not think of perfectionism as a fear, but that is exactly what it is, at its core. We hesitate to try new things because we worry that we might not do them well. So many of us don't go after what we want because we are afraid that we might fail. One of my mantras is "I am willing to risk messing up in order to pursue my dreams." This mentality helps me take the leap and go after what I want, even when I don't feel completely ready or prepared. I didn't know anything about starting a business, but I was willing to learn and makes mistakes along the way in order to bring my dream of opening a yoga studio to life. This same way of thinking helps me in my relationships; I am still learning to ask for what I need, and it feels scary most of the time, but I am doing it anyway. I invite you to take some risks in service of your hopes, dreams, and desires. Let go of perfectionism and be willing to learn along the way. Shifting your thinking in this way will open up all kinds of possibilities and allow you to dream big.

The other way perfectionism shows up for many of us is waiting for perfect conditions before doing something we want to do. I know women who are waiting for ideal conditions for the big things - to date, to have a baby, to quit their jobs, to ask for a divorce, to go back to school - and the smaller things - to try yoga, to reach out to an old friend, to clean out the closet, to learn to cook. Perfection is a myth and when we buy into it, we put our lives on hold. Let's opt out and start going after our dreams - right here, right now inside of our messy, imperfect, *real* lives.

After we work through any blocks that are arising, the next step in **Speak** is to allow yourself to dream! I believe part of self-care is giving yourself permission to want, going after your dreams, and creating a life that feels amazing for you. This will look different for each of us. When it comes to dreaming there is no right or wrong, nothing too big or too small. There is only you, the longings of your heart, and bridging the space between the two. This month's practices and prompts will help you envision your ideal life, name what you want to experience during your lifetime, and gain clarity on how you want to feel inside of your life.

This month you are going to get clear on what you want. This is a powerful piece of bringing your dreams to life but it's important to note that it is just one piece. Unlike some other teachers, I do not believe that we can manifest what we want by simply visualizing it and thinking positively. I believe that visualization and positive thinking are important and I also believe that we need to put in work and meet the Universe halfway.

Also, the idea that we can create our reality through visualization and positive thinking alone ignores the systems that we live inside of, which have a very real impact on our lives and our ability to bring our dreams to fruition. Further, I *know* that bringing our dreams to life is easier for some of us than others based on the privileges we are afforded due to our race, gender, sexuality, socioeconomic status, body size, and more.

After working through any blocks that are arising and getting clear on our hopes, dreams, and desires, we move into the final step of **Speak**: revisiting the process of taking stock that we began in **Release**. Noticing the space between where we want to be and where we currently are allows us to prepare for taking action toward creating the life of our dreams.

Like many people, I intentionally pause and take stock of my life in January. I don't declare resolutions. Instead, I review my goals and consider how I am feeling inside of my life. This process helps me connect with my hopes, dreams, and desires so that I can make plans for the year. I keep my plans loose though because I know that what my heart desires can shift at any time. I recently had an experience where my intuition surprised me with a new dream. In early 2020, I sat down to work on the end of year administrative tasks for my three businesses (the yoga studio, my therapy practice, and the wellness center). As I was working, I heard my inner voice say, "I don't want to do this anymore." She wasn't talking about the bookkeeping; she was talking about running three businesses. For eleven years I had been living my dream of owning and operating a wellness center and then suddenly it didn't feel so dreamy anymore.

We are allowed to change our minds. What once felt like the dream may begin to feel like something else. I was shocked and confused when I first heard the whispers of my intuition telling me to let go of the yoga studio and wellness center. I had so much of my identity wrapped up in those things that I couldn't imagine who I would be without them. Whenever I feel uncertain, I return to my Badass Self-Care practices. I spent more time in meditation. I gave myself space to connect with my wise inner self. I took exquisite care of my body so that I could hear her messages more clearly. I explored my fears and worries with compassion and curiosity. My Badass Self-Care practices supported me in speaking my truth and naming my next dream: selling the wellness center so that I could simplify my work life and focus more on writing and teaching.

This month is meant to be a spark to reignite the burning desires inside of you. I invite you to open up to possibility and allow yourself to want. I believe that there is *something more* than us, call it the Universe/ God/ Source or whatever word makes sense for you, that is both the source of our dreams and an invisible support as we pursue them. Let's invite our hopes, dreams, and desires out to play. Let go of what you think you know and open up to the vulnerable joy of dreaming. Leave space to surprise yourself.

Week 1

PRACTICE:

Chant or sing. Our ability to express what we want is physically and energetically connected to our throat and vocal cords. Chanting and singing are enjoyable and effective techniques for activating the throat center. Don't overthink this. If you are curious about chanting, do some research. If not, simply put on your favorite song and sing! Practice using your voice.

JOURNAL PROMPTS:

What are the messages you have received from family, friends, and society about allowing yourself to want?

What fears come up as you think about naming what you want?

What do you need in order to say yes to dreaming?

MINDFUL MORNING

Journal Practice: Speak

date: ________

The truth is…

I wish…

My intention for today:

Today I will practice self-care by…

MINDFUL EVENING

date: ________

Journal Practice: Speak

The best part of today:

____

____

____

____

The hardest part of today:

____

____

____

____

I'm proud of myself for:

____

____

____

____

Today I supported my intention by:

____

____

____

____

Today I am grateful for:

____

____

____

RELEASE, RESPOND, RECEIVE

Journal Practice

date: ____________

Release: let everything out, write down whatever is on your mind

Respond: pause and connect with your wise self, respond to the things you've written above

Receive: list at least three things you are grateful for in the moment

RELEASE, RESPOND, RECEIVE

Journal Practice

date: ___________

Release: let everything out, write down whatever is on your mind

____
____
____
____
____
____
____
____
____
____

Respond: pause and connect with your wise self, respond to the things you've written above

____
____
____
____
____

Receive: list at least three things you are grateful for in the moment

____
____
____
____
____

MINDFUL MORNING

Journal Practice: Speak

date: ______

The truth is…

I wish…

My intention for today:

Today I will practice self-care by…

MINDFUL EVENING

date: ____________

Journal Practice: Speak

The best part of today:

The hardest part of today:

I'm proud of myself for:

Today I supported my intention by:

Today I am grateful for:

RELEASE, RESPOND, RECEIVE

Journal Practice

date: ________

Release: let everything out, write down whatever is on your mind

____
____
____
____
____
____
____
____
____
____

Respond: pause and connect with your wise self, respond to the things you've written above

____
____
____
____
____

Receive: list at least three things you are grateful for in the moment

____
____
____
____
____

RELEASE, RESPOND, RECEIVE

Journal Practice

date: ____________

Release: let everything out, write down whatever is on your mind

Respond: pause and connect with your wise self, respond to the things you've written above

Receive: list at least three things you are grateful for in the moment

Use this space to free write, draw, or collage.

Use this space to free write, draw, or collage.

Week 2

PRACTICE:

Ideal day. Imagine it is five years from now and your life is everything you ever wanted it to be. You have plenty of money, you love what you do every day, and your relationships are warm and thriving. Allow yourself to visualize what a day inside of your ideal life looks and feels like. Where do you live? When do you wake up to start your day? What do you wear? Who do you spend time with? What activities make up your day? How do you care for yourself throughout the day? What do you eat? Who do you share your meals with? What do you do to unwind in the evening? Take some time to visualize your ideal day in your mind's eye and then write it out below.

My ideal day…

JOURNAL PROMPTS:

In This Life List: What do you want to experience during your lifetime?

How do you want to feel inside of your life?

MINDFUL MORNING

date: ______

Journal Practice: Speak

The truth is…

I wish…

My intention for today:

Today I will practice self-care by…

MINDFUL EVENING

date: ____________

Journal Practice: Speak

The best part of today:

The hardest part of today:

I'm proud of myself for:

Today I supported my intention by:

Today I am grateful for:

RELEASE, RESPOND, RECEIVE

Journal Practice

date: ________

Release: let everything out, write down whatever is on your mind

Respond: pause and connect with your wise self, respond to the things you've written above

Receive: list at least three things you are grateful for in the moment

RELEASE, RESPOND, RECEIVE

Journal Practice

date: ____________

Release: let everything out, write down whatever is on your mind

Respond: pause and connect with your wise self, respond to the things you've written above

Receive: list at least three things you are grateful for in the moment

MINDFUL MORNING

Journal Practice: Speak

date: ____________

The truth is…

I wish…

My intention for today:

Today I will practice self-care by…

MINDFUL EVENING

Journal Practice: Speak

date: ____________

The best part of today:

The hardest part of today:

I'm proud of myself for:

Today I supported my intention by:

Today I am grateful for:

RELEASE, RESPOND, RECEIVE

Journal Practice

date: __________

Release: let everything out, write down whatever is on your mind

Respond: pause and connect with your wise self, respond to the things you've written above

Receive: list at least three things you are grateful for in the moment

RELEASE, RESPOND, RECEIVE

Journal Practice

date: ____________

Release: let everything out, write down whatever is on your mind

Respond: pause and connect with your wise self, respond to the things you've written above

Receive: list at least three things you are grateful for in the moment

YOU

ARE

WORTHY.

Week 3

PRACTICE:

Create a vision board. Visioning is the process of creating a visual representation of what you want. You will need a stack of magazines, scissors, glue, and paper or posterboard. Flip through your magazines and cut out words and images that represent what you want to call into your life. Include specific dreams or goals as well as feelings. Let yourself have fun with this! Stay open to possibility and the magic of discovering the messages and dreams waiting within the magazines. Allow yourself to clip anything that pulls you in, even if (especially if!) it doesn't make sense right now. When you feel ready glue your words and images down. Hang your vision board where you will see it daily to remind you of your hopes and dreams.

JOURNAL PROMPTS:

If I didn't have to do it perfectly, I would…

If money were no object, I would…

If I knew I couldn't fail, I would…

I want ______________________________.

I want ______________________________.

I want ______________________________.

I want ______________________________.

I want ______________________________.

I want ______________________________.

I want ______________________________.

I want ______________________________.

I want ______________________________.

I want ______________________________.

I want ______________________________.

I want ______________________________.

I want ______________________________.

I want ______________________________.

I want ______________________________.

I want ______________________________.

MINDFUL MORNING

Journal Practice: Speak

date: ________

The truth is…

I wish…

My intention for today:

Today I will practice self-care by…

MINDFUL EVENING

Journal Practice: Speak

date: ____________

The best part of today:

The hardest part of today:

I'm proud of myself for:

Today I supported my intention by:

Today I am grateful for:

RELEASE, RESPOND, RECEIVE

Journal Practice

date: ______

Release: let everything out, write down whatever is on your mind

Respond: pause and connect with your wise self, respond to the things you've written above

Receive: list at least three things you are grateful for in the moment

RELEASE, RESPOND, RECEIVE

Journal Practice

date: ____________

Release: let everything out, write down whatever is on your mind

Respond: pause and connect with your wise self, respond to the things you've written above

Receive: list at least three things you are grateful for in the moment

MINDFUL MORNING

Journal Practice: Speak

date: ________

The truth is…

I wish…

My intention for today:

Today I will practice self-care by…

MINDFUL EVENING

date:

Journal Practice: Speak

The best part of today:

The hardest part of today:

I'm proud of myself for:

Today I supported my intention by:

Today I am grateful for:

RELEASE, RESPOND, RECEIVE

Journal Practice

date: ____________

Release: let everything out, write down whatever is on your mind

Respond: pause and connect with your wise self, respond to the things you've written above

Receive: list at least three things you are grateful for in the moment

RELEASE, RESPOND, RECEIVE

Journal Practice

date: ____________

Release: let everything out, write down whatever is on your mind

Respond: pause and connect with your wise self, respond to the things you've written above

Receive: list at least three things you are grateful for in the moment

Use this space to free write, draw, or collage.

Use this space to free write, draw, or collage.

Week 4

PRACTICE:

Write a letter to your future self. You have done a lot of big-picture dreaming so far this month. This week I am inviting you to begin to name your short term dreams or goals. Write a letter to your future self and describe your life as it is one year from now. You can do this by hand and put the letter in a sealed envelope dated one year from now or you can use the website futureme.org and they will email you the letter in one year. I've done this practice several times and I am always amazed at how many of my dreams have come to fruition.

JOURNAL PROMPTS:

What has helped you create change in the past? What are your strengths that you can tap into to move toward your ideal life?

Take stock of where you are now and name where you would like to be. I'll invite you to consider 9 areas of your life. Write a few words or phrases to describe how you feel about each area currently and how you would ideally like to feel/ be. Feel free to use your journal if you need additional space. You may want to skip some of these if they don't feel relevant and/ or add some others.

	Now	*Ideal*
Mind – your thoughts, beliefs, self-talk, intellectual stimulation		
Body - physical wellbeing, energy, vitality		
Soul - heart, spirit, emotions, spirituality		
Home - your home environment		
Work - in or outside of the home, whatever you consider your life's work		
Play - leisure, travel, fun, creativity		
Relationships - family, friends, romantic		
Self-Care - how you care for yourself		

	Now	*Ideal*
Community Care - how you care for others, might include service or activism		
Other		

Look back over your responses to this month's prompts. What themes do you notice? What ideas or feelings are found throughout your responses?

Look back over your responses to this month's prompts. What short-term goals can you create to help move you toward your big dreams? For example, if your big dream is to travel more, a short-term goal might be to start a savings account or if your big dream is to be an herbalist, a short-term goal might be to buy a book about herbalism.

My Big Dream: ______________________________

A short-term goal: ______________________________

My Big Dream: ______________________________

A short-term goal: ______________________________

My Big Dream: ______________________________

A short-term goal: ______________________________

My Big Dream: ______________________________

A short-term goal: ______________________________

My Big Dream: ______________________________

A short-term goal: ___

My Big Dream: ___

A short-term goal: ___

My Big Dream: ___

A short-term goal: ___

My Big Dream: ___

A short-term goal: ___

My Big Dream: ___

A short-term goal ___

My Big Dream: ___

A short-term goal: ___

MINDFUL MORNING

date: ____________

Journal Practice: Speak

The truth is…

I wish…

My intention for today:

Today I will practice self-care by…

MINDFUL EVENING

date: ____________

Journal Practice: Speak

The best part of today:

The hardest part of today:

I'm proud of myself for:

Today I supported my intention by:

Today I am grateful for:

RELEASE, RESPOND, RECEIVE

Journal Practice

date: ___________

Release: let everything out, write down whatever is on your mind

Respond: pause and connect with your wise self, respond to the things you've written above

Receive: list at least three things you are grateful for in the moment

RELEASE, RESPOND, RECEIVE

Journal Practice

date: ____________

Release: let everything out, write down whatever is on your mind

Respond: pause and connect with your wise self, respond to the things you've written above

Receive: list at least three things you are grateful for in the moment

MINDFUL MORNING

Journal Practice: Speak

date: ____________

The truth is…

I wish…

My intention for today:

Today I will practice self-care by…

MINDFUL EVENING

date:

Journal Practice: Speak

The best part of today:

The hardest part of today:

I'm proud of myself for:

Today I supported my intention by:

Today I am grateful for:

RELEASE, RESPOND, RECEIVE

Journal Practice

date: ___________

Release: let everything out, write down whatever is on your mind

Respond: pause and connect with your wise self, respond to the things you've written above

Receive: list at least three things you are grateful for in the moment

RELEASE, RESPOND, RECEIVE

Journal Practice

date: ____________

Release: let everything out, write down whatever is on your mind

Respond: pause and connect with your wise self, respond to the things you've written above

Receive: list at least three things you are grateful for in the moment

Keep track of the days you complete a self-care practice by making a mark in the chart below. Let go of any perfectionism and instead allow this chart to be a celebration of the time and energy you are putting toward your Badass Self-Care practices.

	Journal writing	Meditation	Walking or other movement	Other
1	○	○	○	○
2	○	○	○	○
3	○	○	○	○
4	○	○	○	○
5	○	○	○	○
6	○	○	○	○
7	○	○	○	○
8	○	○	○	○
9	○	○	○	○
10	○	○	○	○
11	○	○	○	○
12	○	○	○	○
13	○	○	○	○
14	○	○	○	○
15	○	○	○	○
16	○	○	○	○
17	○	○	○	○
18	○	○	○	○
19	○	○	○	○
20	○	○	○	○
21	○	○	○	○
22	○	○	○	○
23	○	○	○	○
24	○	○	○	○
25	○	○	○	○
26	○	○	○	○
27	○	○	○	○
28	○	○	○	○
29	○	○	○	○
30	○	○	○	○
31	○	○	○	○

Things I noticed this month...

FURTHER RESOURCES

Finding Your Own North Star by Martha Beck
The Gifts of Imperfection by Brene Brown
The Artist's Way by Julia Cameron
Creative Visualization by Shakti Gawain
Big Magic by Elizabeth Gilbert
The Crossroads of Should and Must by Elle Luna

CHAPTER FIVE

Act

The fifth component of Badass Self-Care is **Act**. This month focuses on taking action toward creating the life you want to live. **Act** includes taking steps toward the dreams you named during **Speak**, as well as creating supportive structure in your life. Topics include setting up routines and rituals to support you as you move toward your dreams and creating boundaries to protect your time and energy. This month is all about building a life where you are regularly tuned into yourself, connected with what you want, and taking steps toward it.

Let's begin with the process that I use to bring my dreams to life. It works for all dreams, big or small. I have used these steps for everything from writing a book to redecorating my dining room. My process includes choosing one thing to focus on, finding the feeling inside the dream, creating action steps, taking action, and grounding back into gratitude.

The first step is to pick one thing to focus on. This is the part I resist! There are so many beautiful dreams swirling around in my head and I want to bring them all to life. And I can. *Just not all at once.* Let your intuition guide you as you choose what you want to focus on. Leave behind any ideas about right or wrong and allow yourself to follow your heart. Remember, a dream can be anything you want to experience: getting a new tattoo, becoming a yoga teacher, going on a vacation or retreat, decluttering your closet, starting a business, knitting a scarf, presenting at a conference, spending more time with your family, making new friends, or starting a blog. Nothing is too big or too small.

After you've decided on your one thing, the next step is to identify the feeling inside the dream. Why do you want what you want? How do you imagine you will feel when your dream comes to fruition? Every dream that we have is really a yearning for a feeling. When we dream of quitting our jobs, we are dreaming of feeling free or happy or empowered. When we dream of running a half marathon, we are dreaming of feeling strong or confident or vibrant. Finding the feeling inside the dream helps us get to the "why" of our desires. The "why" connects our specific dream to the big picture of our lives. The feeling inside the dream is the link between the actions we take today and the lives we are working to create.

Focusing on the feeling inside the dream creates room for possibility because there are many ways to experience the feelings we are craving. For example, if you're seeking the feeling of freedom and your dream is to quit your job, you may actually quit your job or you might take a new role in your company or get a new supervisor or start working from home. There are many different paths to the feeling and the feeling is the ultimate dream. I like to focus on the *feeling inside the dream* and leave room for the Universe to surprise me with other possibilities. We will be focusing on and taking steps toward our specific dreams *and* we will leave room for other avenues to open up. **Act** is a dance of co-creation with the Universe.

Next, we move on to creating action steps. In every dream brought to life there are tens, maybe hundreds, of tiny action steps. I encourage you to break your action steps down into micro-movements that feel totally doable. For example, if your one thing is to start a business, some action steps may be to start a business journal to hold your ideas, brainstorm business names, and research different website platforms. If your one thing is to make new friends, some action steps might be to make a list of your interests, google local classes or events that are aligned with those interests, and plan to go to a class or event.

After identifying several action steps, we begin to take action. Our dreams deserve our time and attention. I am inviting you to take action in a gentle manner that allows you to honor your limits and continue your self-care practices. Capitalism and productivity culture tell us that we need to always be "on" and hustling toward our goals. The Badass Self-Care component of **Act** grows out of the foundation of **Listen**, **Ground**, and **Release**. The actions that we take are rooted in our connection with our inner wise self, a loving relationship with our bodies, and a letting go of beliefs about needing to earn our worth. Because all dreams are really about a feeling, I encourage you to take action toward your dreams in a way that lets you feel the way you want to feel. The goal is for the journey to feel similar to the destination. Don't sacrifice your peace or joy to get shit done. Pushing through to achieve is the old way. Action rooted in self-love and self-care is the new way.

Structure supports us as we take steps toward our dreams. This month I will invite you to create some structure by naming *when* you will take action and *for how long* (e.g., I will write on Fridays from 11am-12pm or I will spend 15 minutes decluttering every day at 7pm). I like to infuse my action steps with a feeling of sacredness. This can be as simple as lighting a candle while you write or creating a playlist to listen to during your decluttering time. Let the time you spend working toward your dream be a sacred ritual. Schedule it and infuse it with joy. Show up for yourself and your dream consistently. The creative muse loves predictability - you show up for her regularly and she will show up for you. All dreams are creative, no matter their nature. We are manifesting something that doesn't yet exist, trying to create something - whether it is a feeling or a thing or a relationship. At this point, it's also important to identify people who can support and encourage you as you move toward your dream. As you begin taking action, think of what would feel supportive for you and who can help hold you accountable.

Boundaries are an important part of creating structure to support our dreams. They help us protect our time and energy as we move toward creating a life we love. Boundaries can be with ourselves (e.g., sticking to an earlier bedtime so we can wake up to meditate) or with others (e.g., not answering a phone call during your meditation time). Setting boundaries is challenging for many women because we have been socialized to accommodate others and put ourselves last. The simple act of saying no can evoke intense fear. As a recovering perfectionist and people-pleaser, I understand that setting boundaries may feel difficult or even scary *and* I've also learned from personal experience that boundaries are essential in order to prioritize your needs and desires. Boundary work is a complex topic. The practices and prompts this month are an invitation to bring compassionate awareness to your existing boundaries (or lack thereof) and begin to create some shifts to support you in your self-care journey.

In many ways, boundaries feel like the final frontier of self-care for me. Throughout my life, I have struggled to figure out how boundaries fit in with what feels like my instinctive urge to care for others. Learning that I can care for myself and still be a loving caregiver for others has truly been (and continues to be) my life's work. I spent decades of my life prioritizing other people's feelings and needs to such an extreme that it was harmful to myself. I was an expert at ignoring what I needed physically and emotionally so that I could be there for other people. I even continued this behavior years into my own Badass Self-Care journey. I would care for myself but only after I had taken care of everyone else. I was surviving on the crumbs of my own love and care.

This isn't a sustainable way to live and eventually I ended up in burn out. I had an episode of depression for the first time in a decade, developed health issues, and was physically and emotionally exhausted. The experience of this burn out was a wake-up call for me. I realized I needed to start *truly* prioritizing myself. I made some serious changes to how I was showing up in my life and created new boundaries around everything from my work schedule to my friendships. I am in a much healthier place now *and* setting and sticking to boundaries can still be challenging for me at times. Please remember that boundaries, like all things in Badass Self-Care, are a process. Practice patience with yourself and give yourself permission to learn and grow along the way.

The final step in this process is to ground back into gratitude. One of the most powerful things we can do while working toward our dreams is to be thankful for what we already have. Gratitude truly is the secret sauce! Research has demonstrated that practicing gratitude helps people feel more optimistic, feel better about their lives as a whole, and make progress toward their goals. *Consciously naming what you are thankful for* helps create more goodness in your life. We've worked with gratitude throughout this journey and this month we will work with it in a specific way related to our dreams.

This month we move into action. Let's birth those beautiful dreams of yours into reality.

Week 1

PRACTICE:

Pick one thing. Review your responses from **Speak** and choose one thing to focus on this month. A beautiful exercise is to write each of your dreams on a 3x5 card or slip of paper. Create a circle of dreams on the ground and literally step inside of it. Face each dream in turn, tune into your body, and notice how each dream feels. Which dream pulls you in the most? It doesn't have to be something that will come to fruition this month, just the one thing that you want to focus on.

JOURNAL PROMPTS:

My one thing:

What are the feelings inside your dream? How will you feel when you have accomplished your one thing?

What are some ways you can have the feeling inside your dream right now, within the life you already have?

MINDFUL MORNING

Journal Practice: Act

date: ____________

My intention for today:

____

____

____

One self-care step I will take today:

____

____

____

My one thing that I am focusing on this month:

____

____

____

An action step I will take today to move toward my one thing:

____

____

____

The feeling inside my dream:

____

____

____

One way to have that feeling today:

____

____

MINDFUL EVENING

Journal Practice: Act

date: ____________

The best part of today:

____

____

____

The hardest part of today:

____

____

____

I'm proud of myself for:

____

____

____

Did you take action toward your dream today? If so, how did it feel? If not, how did that feel?

____

____

____

____

____

____

Three things I am grateful for in this moment:

____

____

____

RELEASE, RESPOND, RECEIVE

Journal Practice

date: ________

Release: let everything out, write down whatever is on your mind

Respond: pause and connect with your wise self, respond to the things you've written above

Receive: list at least three things you are grateful for in the moment

RELEASE, RESPOND, RECEIVE

Journal Practice

date: ____________

Release: let everything out, write down whatever is on your mind

Respond: pause and connect with your wise self, respond to the things you've written above

Receive: list at least three things you are grateful for in the moment

MINDFUL MORNING

Journal Practice: Act

date: ________

My intention for today:

___
___
___

One self-care step I will take today:

___
___
___

My one thing that I am focusing on this month:

___
___
___

An action step I will take today to move toward my one thing:

___
___
___

The feeling inside my dream:

___
___
___

One way to have that feeling today:

___
___

MINDFUL EVENING

date: ______

Journal Practice: Act

The best part of today:

The hardest part of today:

I'm proud of myself for:

Did you take action toward your dream today? If so, how did it feel? If not, how did that feel?

Three things I am grateful for in this moment:

RELEASE, RESPOND, RECEIVE

Journal Practice

date: ____________

Release: let everything out, write down whatever is on your mind

Respond: pause and connect with your wise self, respond to the things you've written above

Receive: list at least three things you are grateful for in the moment

RELEASE, RESPOND, RECEIVE

Journal Practice

date: ____________

Release: let everything out, write down whatever is on your mind

Respond: pause and connect with your wise self, respond to the things you've written above

Receive: list at least three things you are grateful for in the moment

Use this space to free write, draw, or collage.

Use this space to free write, draw, or collage.

Week 2

PRACTICE:

Create a Master Gratitude List. List at least fifty things you are grateful for:

JOURNAL PROMPTS:

Let's begin to think about how you can take action toward your dream. I like to start with a list. Jot down whatever steps come to mind for you right now. You can always return to and expand upon your list at a later date. I prefer to make my action steps as small and simple as possible. Using the example of starting a business, a big step like "build a social media following" feels overwhelming and can actually impede your progress whereas a smaller step such as "make a list of topics for social media posts" feels doable and encourages you to take action.

1. ______________________________
2. ______________________________
3. ______________________________
4. ______________________________
5. ______________________________
6. ______________________________
7. ______________________________
8. ______________________________
9. ______________________________
10. ______________________________
11. ______________________________
12. ______________________________
13. ______________________________
14. ______________________________
15. ______________________________

Which action steps feel like they will be easiest to complete?

Which action steps feel like they will be the most impactful?

Which action steps do you feel most excited about?

How would you like to be supported as you take steps toward your dream?

Who can offer you the type of support you are seeking? Consider friends and family as well as any professional supports (e.g., a therapist, consultant, or coach).

MINDFUL MORNING

Journal Practice: Act

date: ______

My intention for today:

One self-care step I will take today:

My one thing that I am focusing on this month:

An action step I will take today to move toward my one thing:

The feeling inside my dream:

One way to have that feeling today:

MINDFUL EVENING

Journal Practice: Act

date: ____________

The best part of today:

____

____

____

The hardest part of today:

____

____

____

I'm proud of myself for:

____

____

____

Did you take action toward your dream today? If so, how did it feel? If not, how did that feel?

____

____

____

____

____

____

Three things I am grateful for in this moment:

____

____

____

RELEASE, RESPOND, RECEIVE

Journal Practice

date: ____________

Release: let everything out, write down whatever is on your mind

Respond: pause and connect with your wise self, respond to the things you've written above

Receive: list at least three things you are grateful for in the moment

RELEASE, RESPOND, RECEIVE

Journal Practice

date: ____________

Release: let everything out, write down whatever is on your mind

Respond: pause and connect with your wise self, respond to the things you've written above

Receive: list at least three things you are grateful for in the moment

MINDFUL MORNING

Journal Practice: Act

date: ___________

My intention for today:

One self-care step I will take today:

My one thing that I am focusing on this month:

An action step I will take today to move toward my one thing:

The feeling inside my dream:

One way to have that feeling today:

MINDFUL EVENING

Journal Practice: Act

date: ____________

The best part of today:

____

____

____

The hardest part of today:

____

____

____

I'm proud of myself for:

____

____

____

Did you take action toward your dream today? If so, how did it feel? If not, how did that feel?

____

____

____

____

____

____

Three things I am grateful for in this moment:

____

____

____

RELEASE, RESPOND, RECEIVE

Journal Practice

date: ____________

Release: let everything out, write down whatever is on your mind

Respond: pause and connect with your wise self, respond to the things you've written above

Receive: list at least three things you are grateful for in the moment

RELEASE, RESPOND, RECEIVE

Journal Practice

date: ____________

Release: let everything out, write down whatever is on your mind

____
____
____
____
____
____
____
____
____
____

Respond: pause and connect with your wise self, respond to the things you've written above

____
____
____
____
____

Receive: list at least three things you are grateful for in the moment

____
____
____
____
____

YOU'VE

GOT

THIS!

Week 3

PRACTICE

Create a routine to support your dream. Schedule time, daily or weekly, to take action toward your dream. Be specific about what you will do and when you will do it. Consider infusing your routine with something that feels special or sacred (e.g., wearing a certain piece of clothing or jewelry, lighting a candle, or listening to music).

My routine will be:

JOURNAL PROMPTS:

Make a gratitude list related to the dream you are working with this month. What are you thankful for when it comes to your one thing? How is the feeling inside your dream already manifesting in your life?

Taking action toward your dreams sends a powerful message to the Universe. What synchronicities have you experienced lately that let you know you are on the right path?

MINDFUL MORNING

Journal Practice: Act

date: ______

My intention for today:

______
______
______

One self-care step I will take today:

______
______
______

My one thing that I am focusing on this month:

______
______
______

An action step I will take today to move toward my one thing:

______
______
______

The feeling inside my dream:

______
______
______

One way to have that feeling today:

______
______

MINDFUL EVENING

date: ____________

Journal Practice: Act

The best part of today:

The hardest part of today:

I'm proud of myself for:

Did you take action toward your dream today? If so, how did it feel? If not, how did that feel?

Three things I am grateful for in this moment:

RELEASE, RESPOND, RECEIVE

Journal Practice

date: ____________

Release: let everything out, write down whatever is on your mind

Respond: pause and connect with your wise self, respond to the things you've written above

Receive: list at least three things you are grateful for in the moment

RELEASE, RESPOND, RECEIVE

Journal Practice

date: ____________

Release: let everything out, write down whatever is on your mind

Respond: pause and connect with your wise self, respond to the things you've written above

Receive: list at least three things you are grateful for in the moment

MINDFUL MORNING

Journal Practice: Act

date: ____________

My intention for today:

____

____

____

One self-care step I will take today:

____

____

____

My one thing that I am focusing on this month:

____

____

____

An action step I will take today to move toward my one thing:

____

____

____

The feeling inside my dream:

____

____

____

One way to have that feeling today:

____

____

MINDFUL EVENING

date: ______

Journal Practice: Act

The best part of today:

The hardest part of today:

I'm proud of myself for:

Did you take action toward your dream today? If so, how did it feel? If not, how did that feel?

Three things I am grateful for in this moment:

RELEASE, RESPOND, RECEIVE

Journal Practice

date: ________

Release: let everything out, write down whatever is on your mind

Respond: pause and connect with your wise self, respond to the things you've written above

Receive: list at least three things you are grateful for in the moment

RELEASE, RESPOND, RECEIVE

Journal Practice

date: ___________

Release: let everything out, write down whatever is on your mind

Respond: pause and connect with your wise self, respond to the things you've written above

Receive: list at least three things you are grateful for in the moment

Use this space to free write, draw, or collage.

Use this space to free write, draw, or collage.

Week 4

PRACTICE:

Say no. As you prioritize your self-care and take steps toward the life you want to create, there will be times when you want or need to say no to other people's requests. You are allowed to choose yourself. If saying no feels hard, start with saying maybe. This will give you some time to tune into yourself and notice how you really feel about the request. I also want you to know that you are allowed to take back your yes. You have permission to change your mind.

JOURNAL PROMPTS:

Anger, resentment, and jealousy can be great teachers. These emotions often shine a light on the places and ways that we have neglected our needs or abandoned our dreams. Where do you notice anger, resentment, or jealousy arising in your life? What are the lessons these emotions are offering you?

Boundaries are limits you set to protect your time and energy. Consider what boundaries will support you in the following areas as you practice self-care and take steps toward your dream.

Boundaries with myself (e.g., going to bed at a certain time or promising you'll check in with yourself before taking on more commitments):

Boundaries around my work (e.g., not working on Sundays or not checking email after a certain time):

Boundaries in my relationships (e.g., speaking up when someone hurts you or being honest about your capacity to help):

MINDFUL MORNING

Journal Practice: Act

date: ____________

My intention for today:

____

____

____

One self-care step I will take today:

____

____

____

My one thing that I am focusing on this month:

____

____

____

An action step I will take today to move toward my one thing:

____

____

____

The feeling inside my dream:

____

____

____

One way to have that feeling today:

____

____

MINDFUL EVENING

date: ____________

Journal Practice: Act

The best part of today:

The hardest part of today:

I'm proud of myself for:

Did you take action toward your dream today? If so, how did it feel? If not, how did that feel?

Three things I am grateful for in this moment:

RELEASE, RESPOND, RECEIVE

Journal Practice

date: ____________

Release: let everything out, write down whatever is on your mind

Respond: pause and connect with your wise self, respond to the things you've written above

Receive: list at least three things you are grateful for in the moment

RELEASE, RESPOND, RECEIVE

Journal Practice

date: ________

Release: let everything out, write down whatever is on your mind

Respond: pause and connect with your wise self, respond to the things you've written above

Receive: list at least three things you are grateful for in the moment

MINDFUL MORNING

Journal Practice: Act

date: ____________

My intention for today:

____

____

____

One self-care step I will take today:

____

____

____

My one thing that I am focusing on this month:

____

____

____

An action step I will take today to move toward my one thing:

____

____

____

The feeling inside my dream:

____

____

____

One way to have that feeling today:

____

____

MINDFUL EVENING

date:__________

Journal Practice: Act

The best part of today:

The hardest part of today:

I'm proud of myself for:

Did you take action toward your dream today? If so, how did it feel? If not, how did that feel?

Three things I am grateful for in this moment:

RELEASE, RESPOND, RECEIVE

Journal Practice

date: ____________

Release: let everything out, write down whatever is on your mind

Respond: pause and connect with your wise self, respond to the things you've written above

Receive: list at least three things you are grateful for in the moment

RELEASE, RESPOND, RECEIVE

Journal Practice

date: ____________

Release: let everything out, write down whatever is on your mind

Respond: pause and connect with your wise self, respond to the things you've written above

Receive: list at least three things you are grateful for in the moment

Keep track of the days you complete a self-care practice by making a mark in the chart below. Let go of any perfectionism and instead allow this chart to be a celebration of the time and energy you are putting toward your Badass Self-Care practices.

	Journal writing	Meditation	Walking or other movement	Taking action toward your dream	Other
1	○	○	○	○	○
2	○	○	○	○	○
3	○	○	○	○	○
4	○	○	○	○	○
5	○	○	○	○	○
6	○	○	○	○	○
7	○	○	○	○	○
8	○	○	○	○	○
9	○	○	○	○	○
10	○	○	○	○	○
11	○	○	○	○	○
12	○	○	○	○	○
13	○	○	○	○	○
14	○	○	○	○	○
15	○	○	○	○	○
16	○	○	○	○	○
17	○	○	○	○	○
18	○	○	○	○	○
19	○	○	○	○	○
20	○	○	○	○	○
21	○	○	○	○	○
22	○	○	○	○	○
23	○	○	○	○	○
24	○	○	○	○	○
25	○	○	○	○	○
26	○	○	○	○	○
27	○	○	○	○	○
28	○	○	○	○	○
29	○	○	○	○	○
30	○	○	○	○	○
31	○	○	○	○	○

Things I noticed this month...

FURTHER RESOURCES

Managing the Motherload by Rebekah Borucki
The Great Work of Your Life by Stephen Cope
Set Boundaries, Find Peace by Nedra Glover Tawwab
The Set Boundaries Workbook by Nedra Glover Tawwab
The Big Leap by Gay Hendricks
Make Your Creative Dreams Real by SARK

CHAPTER SIX

Honor

The sixth and final component of Badass Self-Care is **Honor**. **Honor** is the practice of claiming our truth, celebrating ourselves, and honoring our feminine nature. Claiming your truth may sound nebulous but it is simply the practice of naming what is true for you. Celebrating yourself is about recognizing who you are and acknowledging your characteristics and accomplishments with joy. Honoring your feminine nature is the practice of unpacking internalized patriarchy and learning to appreciate your feminine aspects.

Claiming your truth is something you can do as loudly or quietly as you like. This is an invitation to tell the truth about your life. You may want to share your story with the world or just write it down in your own journal. Claiming your truth doesn't have to involve anyone else to be powerful. You get to decide who you share your thoughts, feelings, and experiences with. I held so much in for so long that when I began to acknowledge my truth, I believed that I had to share everything all at once in order to be authentic. What I've learned is that that was just another bullshit expectation I had picked up from society. When it comes to claiming your truth, there is no right or wrong. You can keep some things tucked inside your own heart and that doesn't mean that you aren't owning them.

The next piece of **Honor** is celebrating ourselves. Women often struggle with acknowledging themselves and their accomplishments. My hope is that this month's practices and prompts will help you to see just how amazing you truly are! Sometimes we hesitate to celebrate ourselves because of fears around bragging or being egotistical. If you have concerns of that nature, know that you don't have anything to worry about. It's some kind of weird truth that people who worry about those things are definitely not those things. I understand that it might be uncomfortable for you to name things you love and appreciate about yourself. Please don't skip these practices and prompts because they are powerful and will lift you up, just like you lift up other women in your life. Remember you deserve the same love and care that you so generously give to others.

Finally, we circle back to where we began our journey. Badass Self-Care is the practice of unpacking the bullshit messaging of patriarchy so that we can reclaim self-love and self-trust. Reconnecting with our feminine nature is the path back to loving and trusting ourselves. Our journey so far has led us up to this point. Honoring our feminine nature is the culmination of our Badass Self-Care practices. **Honor** is not only about understanding and accepting our feminine aspects but *celebrating* and *revering* them.

We all have feminine and masculine energy inside of us. One is not better than the other; they are simply different. Feminine energy is soft, gentle, and flowing while masculine energy is hard, directive, and linear. Feminine energy invites us to surrender and trust the process, while masculine energy helps us take control and get shit done. Our intuition is feminine in nature, while our rational thought is masculine in nature. Both feminine and masculine energies are necessary and important. However, because we live inside of a patriarchal culture, feminine characteristics are devalued and seen as less than while masculine characteristics are prized and held up as the standard.

The messages and expectations of patriarchy disconnect us from our feminine nature and can lead us to deny or even disown parts of ourselves. We are taught from a young age that being female/feminine is weak, less than, something to be avoided, compensated for, and hidden. This message is so ubiquitous it can be difficult to notice. It is within everything from scolding boys to not be "girly" to tampon commercials assuring us we can maintain our active lifestyles and no one will know we are menstruating, to focusing on the appearances of women in power (rather than their opinions or accomplishments). We can learn to recognize and de-condition ourselves from these messages so that we can reconnect with our feminine aspects and honor ourselves as feminine creatures.

Personally, I lived (unconsciously) from a place of denying my feminine aspects for most of my adult life. I (mis)understood feminism to mean that I could be just like a man and therefore, earn the respect and privileges that come along with being a man. I worked diligently to prove my rational intelligence, drive, and independence. I was hyper-focused on achievement and proving myself. I had rigid expectations of myself and others. I medicated my menstrual cycle and ignored my body's messages. I denounced "women's work" and refused to cook. I was disconnected from nature and her seasons. I ignored the soft whisper of my inner wisdom and followed orders from the deafening patriarchal voice.

I worked hard to embody masculine traits and became successful by masculine standards but instead of feeling fulfilled, I found myself exhausted and feeling empty. I decided to give the soft whisper of my inner wisdom a chance. I started to follow her lead. I began to spend time in spaces she craved and to read books she felt drawn toward. I started to question everything I had previously accepted as "the way it is." I began to understand the connection between being born a girl in this society and feeling innately flawed. I saw through all the lies I had been fed and wept for all the ways I had disowned parts of myself. I came home to the truth that my feminine nature is a gift to be honored.

I realized that I didn't have to perform anymore; I didn't have to try to emulate masculine characteristics in order to prove my worth. I could be my feminine self and be enough, more than enough. I developed a new understanding of feminism: that I deserve equal respect, rights, and privileges *as I am* - to be honored as a woman in her own right. I reclaimed the parts of myself that I had abandoned and began to honor myself as a feminine creature. I started to embrace my feminine aspects. I gained an understanding that my sensitivity is a gift. I began tracking my menstrual cycle and adjusting my life to honor my needs at different times of the month. I connected with the Moon and her cycles. I discovered that I love to bake and that I had a long-ignored desire to make my home beautiful. I spent more time in nature and allowed myself to rest. I deepened my connection with my inner wisdom.

I most often experience my feminine energy as a wise inner voice. What was once a soft whisper has become a strong and steady guide in my daily life. Now that I am connected with and honor my feminine energy, I cannot imagine living without her amazing guidance. My feminine energy makes things beautiful, juicy, and fulfilling. She invites me to slow down and let go; she helps me surrender and trust life. She makes my life feel deeper and more connected, *more alive.*

The truth is I sometimes still fall back into my old ways of being. In fact, I reverted to my old masculine ways while I was working on finalizing this chapter about honoring our feminine nature. The Universe often has quite a sense of humor when delivering lessons! I had set a deadline for myself, and I was pushing hard to finish. While masculine energy is helpful for completing a big project, I was so deep in it that it became harmful. I wasn't allowing myself to rest. I was trying to control the creative process, rather than surrender to it. Eventually, my stress and anxiety became overwhelming and I had a meltdown. I let myself crumble into a crying ball of frustration and fear and from there, I was able to find my way back to my wise inner self by meditating and writing in my journal. As always, she had all the answers I needed and the rest of this chapter flowed effortlessly once I took her advice.

This experience was a powerful reminder that there is no end point when it comes to the practice of reclaiming self-love and self-trust. In fact, slipping back into old ways of being is a natural part of the process of change. How we respond to ourselves when we fall back into old ways of being is a beautiful indicator of our growth. I was able to greet myself with compassion and curiosity rather than shame and judgment. My hope is that you are able to do the same for yourself as you continue on this path.

Our final month in the Badass Self-Care journey focuses on claiming your truth, celebrating yourself, and honoring your feminine nature. You may already have some experience with the practices that make up **Honor** or they might be new ideas and ways of being that you are just getting started with. Wherever you are on your journey, this month's practices and prompts will help you deepen your love and appreciation for yourself as a feminine creature.

Week 1

PRACTICE:

Embrace your *whole* self. Humans are complex creatures. **Honor** asks us to find love and compassion for all the parts of ourselves. Take some time this week to reflect on all the parts of you. You could do this by meditating on the question, "Who am I?" or making a list using the prompt "I am" or you could paint, draw, or collage a visual representation of yourself. However you decide to explore who you are, practice greeting yourself with compassion.

JOURNAL PROMPTS:

What do you feel like you can't say?

What is a truth that you are ready to claim?

What does it mean to you to honor yourself?

Where are you not honoring yourself?

MINDFUL MORNING

Journal Practice: Honor

date: ______

The truth is…

You are worthy. Affirm that for yourself. I deserve...

Today I will honor myself by…

MINDFUL EVENING

date: __________

Journal Practice: Honor

What are you celebrating about yourself today?

Pause and take three deep breaths. Tune into yourself. What are the words you need to hear right now? Write them here:

Three things I am grateful for in this moment:

RELEASE, RESPOND, RECEIVE

Journal Practice

date: ____________

Release: let everything out, write down whatever is on your mind

Respond: pause and connect with your wise self, respond to the things you've written above

Receive: list at least three things you are grateful for in the moment

RELEASE, RESPOND, RECEIVE

Journal Practice

date: ____________

Release: let everything out, write down whatever is on your mind

Respond: pause and connect with your wise self, respond to the things you've written above

Receive: list at least three things you are grateful for in the moment

MINDFUL MORNING

Journal Practice: Honor

date: ____________

The truth is…

You are worthy. Affirm that for yourself. I deserve...

Today I will honor myself by…

MINDFUL EVENING

date: ____________

Journal Practice: Honor

What are you celebrating about yourself today?

Pause and take three deep breaths. Tune into yourself. What are the words you need to hear right now? Write them here:

Three things I am grateful for in this moment:

RELEASE, RESPOND, RECEIVE

Journal Practice

date: ________

Release: let everything out, write down whatever is on your mind

Respond: pause and connect with your wise self, respond to the things you've written above

Receive: list at least three things you are grateful for in the moment

RELEASE, RESPOND, RECEIVE

Journal Practice

date: ____________

Release: let everything out, write down whatever is on your mind

Respond: pause and connect with your wise self, respond to the things you've written above

Receive: list at least three things you are grateful for in the moment

Use this space to free write, draw, or collage.

Use this space to free write, draw, or collage.

Week 2

PRACTICE:

Celebrate yourself. This week I want you to plan a celebration for yourself. The celebration can be as big or small as feels right for you. You could throw yourself a party or you could celebrate by lighting a candle and taking a bath. The intention behind this practice is for you to pause and celebrate yourself. There doesn't have to be an occasion; you just being you is reason enough to celebrate!

JOURNAL PROMPTS:

What do you love about yourself?

Make a Have Done list. What are the things you have accomplished in your life? Sometimes we get caught up in daily life and we forget to reflect on how far we've come and all that we've done. Take some time to ponder your life and make note of all that you have done.

You are a badass. And I know sometimes you might forget. Make a list of times when you've been brave or strong or resilient or whatever word fits for you. On your hard days, let this list remind you that you are a badass.

Times I've Been ______________________________:

MINDFUL MORNING

date:

Journal Practice: Honor

The truth is…

You are worthy. Affirm that for yourself. I deserve...

Today I will honor myself by…

MINDFUL EVENING

date: ____________

Journal Practice: Honor

What are you celebrating about yourself today?

Pause and take three deep breaths. Tune into yourself. What are the words you need to hear right now? Write them here:

Three things I am grateful for in this moment:

RELEASE, RESPOND, RECEIVE

Journal Practice

date: __________

Release: let everything out, write down whatever is on your mind

Respond: pause and connect with your wise self, respond to the things you've written above

Receive: list at least three things you are grateful for in the moment

RELEASE, RESPOND, RECEIVE

Journal Practice

date: ______________

Release: let everything out, write down whatever is on your mind

Respond: pause and connect with your wise self, respond to the things you've written above

Receive: list at least three things you are grateful for in the moment

MINDFUL MORNING

date: ________

Journal Practice: Honor

The truth is…

____
____
____
____
____
____
____
____

You are worthy. Affirm that for yourself. I deserve...

____
____
____
____
____
____
____
____

Today I will honor myself by…

____
____
____
____
____
____
____

MINDFUL EVENING

date: ___________

Journal Practice: Honor

What are you celebrating about yourself today?

Pause and take three deep breaths. Tune into yourself. What are the words you need to hear right now? Write them here:

Three things I am grateful for in this moment:

RELEASE, RESPOND, RECEIVE

Journal Practice

date: ___________

Release: let everything out, write down whatever is on your mind

Respond: pause and connect with your wise self, respond to the things you've written above

Receive: list at least three things you are grateful for in the moment

RELEASE, RESPOND, RECEIVE

Journal Practice

date: ____________

Release: let everything out, write down whatever is on your mind

Respond: pause and connect with your wise self, respond to the things you've written above

Receive: list at least three things you are grateful for in the moment

YOU

ARE

NOT

ALONE.

Week 3

PRACTICE:

Track your cycle. Learning about and honoring the cycles of my life has changed how I approach my work, social time, and self-care. We are cyclical creatures, impacted by the seasons, the moon cycle, and our menstrual cycle (if we have one). Because I am a menstruating woman, I live and work by my menstrual cycle. I also use the moon cycle as a guide for my intention setting (New Moon) and releasing rituals (Full Moon) each month. If you do not have a menstrual cycle, use the moon cycle as a guide.

If you are tracking using your menstrual cycle, Day 1 is the day you begin your bleed. If you are tracking according to the moon cycle, Day 1 is the New Moon. You can track using a journal or by creating a chart. I like to note my mood and energy levels each day. Jot down anything that feels relevant for you. One month of tracking will give you some insight into how you respond to various parts of your cycle. The longer you track, the more you will come to know yourself and your cycles.

JOURNAL PROMPTS:

What are the messages you have received about femininity?

When are you inside of your feminine energy?

How will you begin to honor your cyclical nature? Some ideas include making a seasonal bucket list, tracking your menstrual cycle, or creating rituals for the New and Full Moons. A simple daily practice is to let go of expecting yourself to show up in the same way every day. Instead, pause and check in with how you feel physically, emotionally, and energetically and make adjustments to honor what you are needing on that particular day.

What does your feminine, intuitive self want you to know?

MINDFUL MORNING

Journal Practice: Honor

date: ________

The truth is…

You are worthy. Affirm that for yourself. I deserve...

Today I will honor myself by…

MINDFUL EVENING

date: __________

Journal Practice: Honor

What are you celebrating about yourself today?

Pause and take three deep breaths. Tune into yourself. What are the words you need to hear right now? Write them here:

Three things I am grateful for in this moment:

RELEASE, RESPOND, RECEIVE

Journal Practice

date: ___________

Release: let everything out, write down whatever is on your mind

Respond: pause and connect with your wise self, respond to the things you've written above

Receive: list at least three things you are grateful for in the moment

RELEASE, RESPOND, RECEIVE

Journal Practice

date: ___________

Release: let everything out, write down whatever is on your mind

Respond: pause and connect with your wise self, respond to the things you've written above

Receive: list at least three things you are grateful for in the moment

MINDFUL MORNING

Journal Practice: Honor

date:__________

The truth is…

You are worthy. Affirm that for yourself. I deserve...

Today I will honor myself by…

MINDFUL EVENING

date: ____________

Journal Practice: Honor

What are you celebrating about yourself today?

Pause and take three deep breaths. Tune into yourself. What are the words you need to hear right now? Write them here:

Three things I am grateful for in this moment:

RELEASE, RESPOND, RECEIVE

Journal Practice

date: ___________

Release: let everything out, write down whatever is on your mind

Respond: pause and connect with your wise self, respond to the things you've written above

Receive: list at least three things you are grateful for in the moment

RELEASE, RESPOND, RECEIVE

Journal Practice

date: ____________

Release: let everything out, write down whatever is on your mind

Respond: pause and connect with your wise self, respond to the things you've written above

Receive: list at least three things you are grateful for in the moment

Use this space to free write, draw, or collage.

Use this space to free write, draw, or collage.

Week 4

PRACTICE:

Your choice. Take some time to get quiet and tune into yourself. How can you honor yourself this week? Everything that you need is already within you. Let your wise inner teacher be your guide.

JOURNAL PROMPTS:

Who were you six months ago when you started this journey? What was happening in your world? What inspired you to pick up this book?

What has shifted in the last six months?

Who are you now? How did you arrive here?

What practices will you continue, to honor this new version of yourself?

Who do you want to become? What's next for you?

What do you need to support this vision of yourself?

MINDFUL MORNING

date: ________

Journal Practice: Honor

The truth is…

You are worthy. Affirm that for yourself. I deserve...

Today I will honor myself by…

MINDFUL EVENING

date:

Journal Practice: Honor

What are you celebrating about yourself today?

Pause and take three deep breaths. Tune into yourself. What are the words you need to hear right now? Write them here:

Three things I am grateful for in this moment:

RELEASE, RESPOND, RECEIVE

Journal Practice

date: ____________

Release: let everything out, write down whatever is on your mind

Respond: pause and connect with your wise self, respond to the things you've written above

Receive: list at least three things you are grateful for in the moment

RELEASE, RESPOND, RECEIVE

Journal Practice

date: ____________

Release: let everything out, write down whatever is on your mind

Respond: pause and connect with your wise self, respond to the things you've written above

Receive: list at least three things you are grateful for in the moment

MINDFUL MORNING

date: ________

Journal Practice: Honor

The truth is…

____
____
____
____
____
____
____
____

You are worthy. Affirm that for yourself. I deserve...

____
____
____
____
____
____
____
____

Today I will honor myself by…

____
____
____
____
____
____
____

MINDFUL EVENING

date: ______

Journal Practice: Honor

What are you celebrating about yourself today?

Pause and take three deep breaths. Tune into yourself. What are the words you need to hear right now? Write them here:

Three things I am grateful for in this moment:

RELEASE, RESPOND, RECEIVE

Journal Practice

date: ___________

Release: let everything out, write down whatever is on your mind

Respond: pause and connect with your wise self, respond to the things you've written above

Receive: list at least three things you are grateful for in the moment

RELEASE, RESPOND, RECEIVE

Journal Practice

date: ____________

Release: let everything out, write down whatever is on your mind

Respond: pause and connect with your wise self, respond to the things you've written above

Receive: list at least three things you are grateful for in the moment

Keep track of the days you complete a self-care practice by making a mark in the chart below. Let go of any perfectionism and instead allow this chart to be a celebration of the time and energy you are putting toward your Badass Self-Care practices.

	Journal writing	Meditation	Walking or other movement	Other
1	○	○	○	○
2	○	○	○	○
3	○	○	○	○
4	○	○	○	○
5	○	○	○	○
6	○	○	○	○
7	○	○	○	○
8	○	○	○	○
9	○	○	○	○
10	○	○	○	○
11	○	○	○	○
12	○	○	○	○
13	○	○	○	○
14	○	○	○	○
15	○	○	○	○
16	○	○	○	○
17	○	○	○	○
18	○	○	○	○
19	○	○	○	○
20	○	○	○	○
21	○	○	○	○
22	○	○	○	○
23	○	○	○	○
24	○	○	○	○
25	○	○	○	○
26	○	○	○	○
27	○	○	○	○
28	○	○	○	○
29	○	○	○	○
30	○	○	○	○
31	○	○	○	○

Things I noticed this month...

FURTHER RESOURCES

The Book of SHE by Sara Avant Stover
Untamed by Glennon Doyle
Code Red by Lisa Lister
Love Your Lady Landscape by Lisa Lister
Women Who Run with the Wolves by Clarissa Pinkola Estés
Lunar Abundance by Ezzie Spencer

This is Not an Ending

Congratulations on working your way through this book! Thank you for allowing me to be your guide on the path toward reclaiming self-love and self-trust.

While this is the end of the book, this is not an *ending*. My hope is that your Badass Self Care journey will be an ongoing process. At this point, you likely have some practices that feel like second nature. You also likely have some areas you would like to continue to work on. The work of reclaiming self-love and self-trust is not something you can complete and check off your to-do list; it is an ongoing, ever-evolving process of being in relationship with yourself. I hope you will continue to invest time and energy into your self-care. I encourage you to come back to these pages often and revisit the practices and prompts. I find that the same practices and prompts land differently based on where I am in my life. There is always more to discover on this journey and that is good news!

I invite you to complete the Badass Self-Care Assessment below and then flip back to page five and compare it to the assessment you completed at the start of this journey. As you complete and compare your assessments, let go of any judgment that arises. Instead of categorizing yourself or your practices as good or bad, try just observing with curiosity and compassion.

Listen

Turning inward and connecting with ourselves.

	Never	*Rarely*	*Some-times*	*Often*	*Almost Always*
I spend time turned inward, connecting with myself.					
My intuition guides my choices.					
I meditate.					
I have difficulty hearing my inner voice.					
I trust myself.					
I follow my gut.					

Ground

Cultivating a loving relationship with our bodies.

	Never	*Rarely*	*Some-times*	*Often*	*Almost Always*
I know when I am thirsty.					
I eat when I am hungry.					
I get 7-9 hours of sleep per night.					
I know what kind of movement feels good in my body.					
I am dissatisfied with the size or shape of my body.					
I engage in a regular movement/ physical activity practice.					
I appreciate my body.					
I understand how the media influences my feelings about my body.					

Release

Letting go of what no longer serves us.

	Never	*Rarely*	*Some-times*	*Often*	*Almost Always*
I hold on to things.					
Thoughts replay in my mind over and over.					
My living space feels peaceful and orderly.					
It is hard for me to forgive myself.					
My life is aligned with my priorities.					
I have habits I'd like to change.					
I have tools or practices for releasing my emotions and cleansing my energy.					

Speak

Naming our desires and allowing ourselves to want.

	Never	*Rarely*	*Some-times*	*Often*	*Almost Always*
I believe I am allowed to want.					
I have clarity around my dreams and goals.					
I know what I want.					
I have trouble speaking up for myself.					
My needs matter.					
My dreams and goals are important.					

Act

Taking steps toward our dreams and creating supportive structure in our lives.

	Never	*Rarely*	*Some-times*	*Often*	*Almost Always*
I set boundaries to protect my time and energy.					
I create action plans to help me work toward my goals.					
It's hard for me to say no.					
I worry about letting others down.					
I take time for myself.					
I pursue my dreams.					

Honor

Claiming our truth, celebrating ourselves, and honoring our feminine nature.

	Never	*Rarely*	*Some-times*	*Often*	*Almost Always*
I prioritize myself.					
I have to work to earn worthiness.					
I worry about not being good enough.					
I love myself.					
I celebrate my strengths.					
When someone gives me a compliment, I brush it off or qualify it.					
I embrace my feminine characteristics.					

What do you notice as you compare your two assessments?

What are you celebrating as you come to the close of your six-month Badass Self-Care journey?

What are your main takeaways from this journey?

You did it! You devoted at least six months, maybe more, to your Badass Self-Care journey. I am so proud of you!

You learned to turn inward and connect with your wise self. You practiced cultivating a loving relationship with your body. You let go of what was no longer serving you. You named your dreams and began taking action toward them. You celebrated yourself and honored your feminine nature. You unpacked the bullshit messaging of patriarchy and reclaimed self-love and self-trust. You are a badass!

Thank you for being here. I am truly grateful that you chose to join me on this Badass Self-Care journey. May you always remember that you are worthy of love and care.

Acknowledgments

I've had the privilege of wonderful professional and personal support while writing this book. I'd like to thank Kate Bowie for editing these pages with expertise, humor, and kindness. Your feedback was invaluable and made the book better. Thank you to Jacquelyn Tierney for your gorgeous design of the interior pages and book cover. You are brilliant at what you do and a dream to work with.

In creating the Badass Self-Care framework, I have drawn upon my professional training as a psychologist and trauma-informed yoga teacher, as well as my personal life experiences. It feels impossible to list every person who has influenced my thinking, but I am going to try! I want to thank some of the amazing women who have been my teachers in this life: Melinda Alexander, Dr. Catherine Cook-Cottone, Kelly Diels, Hannah Marcotti, and Kimberly Wilson. I have also found great teachers in the pages of books. Specifically, I have been deeply impacted by the work of Brené Brown, Julia Cameron, Eve Ensler, Thich Nhat Hanh, Jean Kilbourne, Audre Lorde, and Sonya Renee Taylor.

Thank you to the hundreds of women who have participated in my Badass Self-Care courses over the years. You have helped shape this work and it is an honor to be in community with you.

I want to thank the many women who read the first draft of chapter one and provided feedback: Stephanie Appenheimer, Lori Chiarmonte, Tomasina Cook, Ceaton Falgiano, Maya Glover Mollerus, Diane Harper Greene, Jenna Myer, April Sauer, Sue Vester, and Jennifer Winarski. Special thanks to Sue Vester for the brilliant idea to break each month's content down into weeks. It transformed the book in the best way!

I am lucky to be surrounded by loving and supportive friends and family. Thank you for understanding when I disappear into my metaphorical writing cave and for always being there when I come back out. I especially want to thank Kimberlee Beach, Nicole Chumsky, Tomasina Cook, and Sue Vester for your ongoing friendship, support, and encouragement.

Whenever I bring one of my dreams to life (like this book), I reflect on the many women who supported me when I was a young single mother. I am deeply grateful to my mom, Elizabeth Smallwood, my grandma Margaret Pittorf, aunt Edith Weaver, and sister, Maureen Remus. I would not be who I am or where I am today without your help. Thank you, thank you, thank you.

To my grandma Margaret Pittorf, you are a powerful source of strength and love in this world. You inspire me and I can only hope to navigate my life with the strength and grace that you've shown. Thank you for reading everything I write and sending me sweet messages about my words. It means more to me than you'll ever know. Mom, you were my first teacher in badassery. Thank you for showing me how to be strong and independent, teaching me that I can be anything I want to be, and most of all, loving me no matter what. To my sister, Maureen, I'm so grateful for your presence in my life. Even though I'm your big sister, I look up to you. Thank you for always being there when I need help or advice.

To my daughters, Megan and Melaina, thank you for your patience as well as encouragement and excitement when it comes to my creative projects. As many words as I write, I don't think I'll ever be able to adequately express how much I love you both. Being your mom is the greatest privilege of my life. Finally, thank you to my husband, Michael Lewis. I am grateful to have a true partner in this life. Your love and support help me be the best version of myself. You have been a healing presence in my life for the past 18 years and I love our life together.

About the Author

Melinda Scime, Ph.D. is a licensed psychologist, certified trauma-informed yoga teacher, and creator of Badass Self-Care®. She is also the author of *My Sacred Pause: Daily reflections on looking within, loving who you are, and living out loud.* Melinda earned her doctorate in Counseling and School Psychology from the University at Buffalo where she studied the mind-body connection and its impact on the healing process. After graduate school, she started Tree of Life Yoga Studio and went on to found Living Wellness of Niagara, a holistic health center in her hometown of Niagara Falls, NY.

Through her private practice as a therapist, books, and online course offerings, Melinda works with sensitive, empathic women who are ready to move beyond exhaustion and overwhelm and into the space of self-care and prioritizing their own needs. Her work is informed by her experience as a therapist and yoga teacher with specialized training in trauma, as well as her lived experience of navigating self-care in this world as a woman, mother, and healer. Her community of badass women is devoted to doing inner work and creating outer change. Learn more about Melinda and her work at www.melindascime.com.

CPSIA information can be obtained
at www.ICGtesting.com
Printed in the USA
FSHW020137091121
85969FS